Orchids in the Cornfield
Collected Writings of the Heartland Women's Writers Guild

Table of Contents

Chapter 1
Bird Songs Bang on the Drums of Daylight

CHAPTER 2
YOUR DADDY IS A PICKER, AIN'T HE GIRL?

CHAPTER 3
HOW DO YOU PUT A FRIEND ON A PIECE OF PAPER?

CHAPTER 4
I ALMOST DROWN IN YOUR TENDER EYES

CHAPTER 5
WITH JOHNNY CASH AS MY WITNESS

CHAPTER 6
TO SEE THINGS MORE CLEARLY

CHAPTER 7
WITH FAITH, WE FLY

CHAPTER 8
LONGING FOR WELL-KNOWN LANDSCAPES

CHAPTER 9
EATING LIVER SAUSAGE ON RYE
IN THE MIDDLE OF THE MISSISSIPPI

CHAPTER 10
I WAS LUCKY TO HAVE BEEN THERE

CHAPTER 11
IN SOLITUDE SHE SUFFERED HER SADNESS

CHAPTER 12
LIFE CANNOT BE LIVED OR MEASURED IN A STRAIGHT LINE

ACKNOWLEDGMENTS

The idea for *Orchids in the Cornfield* was conceived in the spring of 2004 and has been a labor of love for all the women of the Heartland Women's Writers Guild.

This book project was suggested and spearheaded by our own Melany Nitzsche. Her clarity of vision, organization, and communication skills took our book from just a dream to the finished product. We thank her for taking on this herculean project and will always think of her fondly as our "Big Kahuna."

Our appreciation also goes to Ed Madden, our photographer and book designer. His creative ideas and inventive approaches have been invaluable to us.

We wish to acknowledge the staff of Morrison-Talbott Library. They have been ardent supporters of our writing group these past seven years, and graciously provide a room for our monthly meetings.

Our group would never have been formed without Roselyn Mathews' dream of providing a haven for women writers to gather and learn from each other. Thank you, Roselyn.

Finally, we wish to thank our families and friends for their encouragement, patience, and inspiration.

PREFACE

The "soul" of the Heartland Women's Writers Guild came into being in January 1998 when I read an article in a St. Louis newspaper about a women's writers group in Springfield, Illinois called Brainchild. That article became the seed that germinated in my heart and mind, and inspired me to form a similar writers group locally in May 1998. The poetry, essays, journal entries, and short fiction in this book represent the fruit of that seed.

Over the years, participants in our writers guild have come and gone; but the eleven women whose writings are included in *Orchids in the Cornfield* have stayed the course. Their places of birth, backgrounds, ages, careers, and personalities are as diverse as their writing styles. These incidental differences add richness and a broad perspective to the work in this book.

The authors in this anthology were brought together by their passion for writing; however, it is their shared creative inspiration that sustains a palpable, high-energy excitement for their craft. And best of all, along the way, these women have gained the bonus of becoming good friends.

Orchids in the Cornfield is divided into twelve chapters representative of various stages and aspects of life. As you read these chapters, allow your imagination to roam freely with the words and images written in celebration, in grief, in love, and in humor. Awaken your senses to nature as "bird songs bang on the drums of daylight"; color your perspective of adventure by "eating liver sausage on rye in the middle of the Mississippi"; gain an appreciation of your memories, and know that you were "lucky to have been there"; and, in the final analysis, perhaps you will agree that life is an amazing, unpredictable journey that "cannot be lived or measured in a straight line." All these possibilities are our grateful gifts to you, the readers.

– Roselyn Mathews

Waterloo, Illinois
September 2005

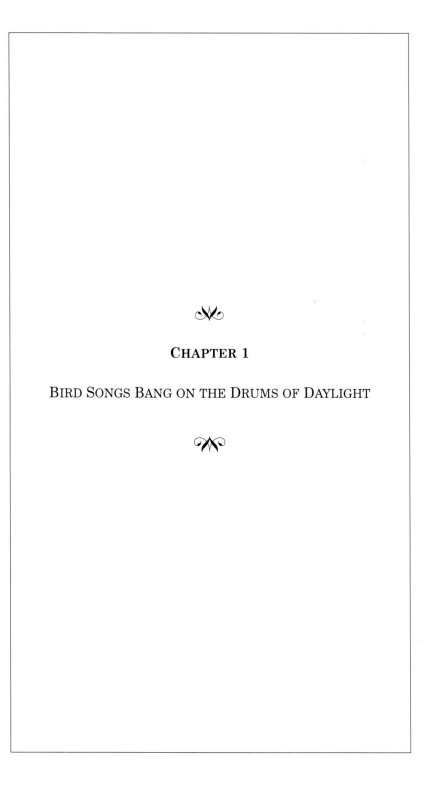

CHAPTER 1

BIRD SONGS BANG ON THE DRUMS OF DAYLIGHT

An Anxious Turn of Season

Bird songs bang
on the drums of daylight
and awaken the world.

A guttural groan
from black-eyed bullfrogs
cranks through the air.

Josi the Labrador
cocks her nose
into the crisp wind.

Bradford Pear petals
dust sap-green lawns
with a snowy bluster.

Rain caps drip
from March's gray
ominous cloudbanks.

Agitated orbs of gnats
whirl outside my window
announcing a storm.

Nature is anxious today
as am I;
spring nears.

— *Lori Becherer*

SENSUOUS SEASON

a lust for Spring
greets me as I awaken
a caress of sunlight
touches my shoulder
and stirs my senses

the sweet intoxicating scent
of purple hyacinths
envelops me
bright yellow daffodils cluster
in secret corners of my mind
they nod and beckon to me

barefoot, I glide effortlessly
over the grass carpet
glistening with early morning dew
and bend down
to listen to a tiny ant

I am dizzily drunk
from the potent nectar
of Spring

– Roselyn Mathews

WILDFLOWER DANCERS

Wildflower dancers
flutter at woodland's edge
serene sunlight embraced
in the solitude of forest
bluebells hum in harmony

Mayapples strum
little boy's breeches
yellow suspenders in tote
twitter to the tune
life pulsates

On buttery nights
when dew drops shimmer
under a smiling moon
a mellow orchestra serenades
where wildflowers dance

– Lori Becherer

2nd Place Southwestern Illinois College
2005 Poetry Contest

NATURE'S UNIVERSE

A JOURNAL ENTRY

In the loveliness of today's sunshine, I find myself relaxing on the patio in my favorite lounge chair. The sun is sharp and the day is bright, though the air seems to beckon that autumn is just beyond the horizon. Intensely dry warmth permeates my skin, unlike the humidity that I tolerate through the early days of summer.

My mind is occupied with the sharp and undeniable songs of nature. Gay crickets lead the band of clicking cicadas, cackling distant birds and whispering wasps that flutter above sedum. A wind chime gently tings her symbols, unified with the sounds of this summer afternoon. A slick southern wind bursts, as a young flowering crab tree tosses her head to the north and the pond flaunts its waving sparkles. A fly sounds off with a vibrating buzz and a snoring Labrador provides a gentle bass drum beat. Nature's jazz band jams in orchestrated rhythm, as only nature knows how.

Without forethought, a lovely checkerspot butterfly has landed beside my leg. With each step forward his antennae tap down checking the path ahead. He is painted with a perfect autumn palette; undertones of deep umber and golden browns, dotted with the sienna reds and rusts of fall mums. Suddenly he rises, landing on my elbow as though he knows I want a closer view. The disproportionately long proboscis rapidly fires while seeking nectar on its new landing pad. The wings keep perfect time – flapping down onto my skin with a gentle pat and then perching upward posed in prayer like a child's hands. I move my hand toward him and he is gone just as quickly as he arrived. I am grateful for the close encounter.

I stare out from my shaded resting spot onto the white blooms of garlic chives that stand with proud heads held high on long green straws. The flurry of activity above the chives tells me that this flower is one of nature's sweetest treats. Perhaps I shall plant more, although it seems to be naturally spreading across my herb garden. My parsley is chewed down to bare stems from the yellow and black caterpillars of the swallowtail.

I observe the small creatures that live off my garden world, and I am aware of how tiny I am to this universe but how large my contribution is to nature.

– Lori Becherer

BEGONIA BLOOM

A pink begonia drops a bloom

while falling catches a thread

suspended in the summer breeze

twirling free upon a twine of web.

– Lori Becherer

RAIN'S GREAT MASQUERADE

A tepid wash of burnt umber
collides with ultramarine
creating a mottled summer palette.

The scent of rain teases a scorched sky.
A fleet of ships cruises east over my head
as masts flail and I wait for the white squall.

The parched earth screams,
her chapped mouth crying for renewal of life.
A muted haze dangles as the sunset burns
through an ethereal stage
and thunder murmurs in the wake.

Moths flutter until lifeless
at the flash of mellow nightlights.
The soulful song from silent sparrows
hangs on the promise of a raindrop.

– Lori Becherer

Autumn Haiku Poems

Summer Dream

Autumn's sun and warmth
 Keep summery dreams alive
  Forbidding winter.

Cliff and Fern's Yard

I face Saturday
 Warmed by favorite flannel
  Rakes and bags in hand.

Neighbors congregate
 Raking, gathering, bagging
  Autumn's legacy.

Autumn Euphony

Kick up crunchy leaves
 Articulating Autumn
  For my thirsting soul.

– Patricia Robert

THANKSGIVING #1

Sudden snow storm
Power fails
Bradford Pear splays into three
       North
  West
    South
Broken under the heavy weight
Of an unexpected burden
Changing again this living landscape

– Melany Nitzsche

TO A SNOWFLAKE

I hold out my scarlet mitten
A frail starry crystal drifts onto it
So light I feel nothing
So innocent, unimportant, harmless
It melts away

But its counterparts
Are bonding together
A multitude float down
From ice filled gray clouds
To cover the earth

The world is transformed, sounds muffled
Wrapped in a whipped cream frosting
Common things take on mysterious shapes
Children slide down Art Hill
Old folks find comfort by their fireside

Frail starry crystals
Have bonded together
To bring delight
To our wintry world

– Elizabeth Hoffman

WINTER HAIKU

Sparrow

sparrow, come and dine
        seeds meant for robins feed you
                let me show mercy

Winter Tree

hidden potential
        deciduous green diamonds
                aching to burst forth

Snow

under silent snow
        hibernating tulip bulbs
                lie awaiting Spring

– Patricia Robert

ICE STORM

The morning of December 31st the little red farm house awoke huddled in an ice shrouded world. As the sun rose, it sent rainbow prisms onto the white kitchen walls. After she finished her coffee, the lone dweller bundled up in her gold parka and stepped out the back door.

Then she heard the sounds, first myriad tinkles like icy wind chimes in the trees. As the sun grew warmer, she heard clanking as glistening chunks of ice began to fall to the ground until the lawn looked like a giant jeweler's velvet piled with iridescent unset diamonds.

They shattered under her feet as she carefully picked her way across the yard to check the woodpile. It looked like a modern glass sculpture glowing in the sun. No wood for the fireplace there.

Then the sounds became different...a crack as a small branch broke, loud reports as larger branches crashed to the ground. From the woods beyond the pasture came a constant volley of pistol-like reports.

Still she stood outside, awed by the beauty and violence of the moment.

– Elizabeth Hoffman

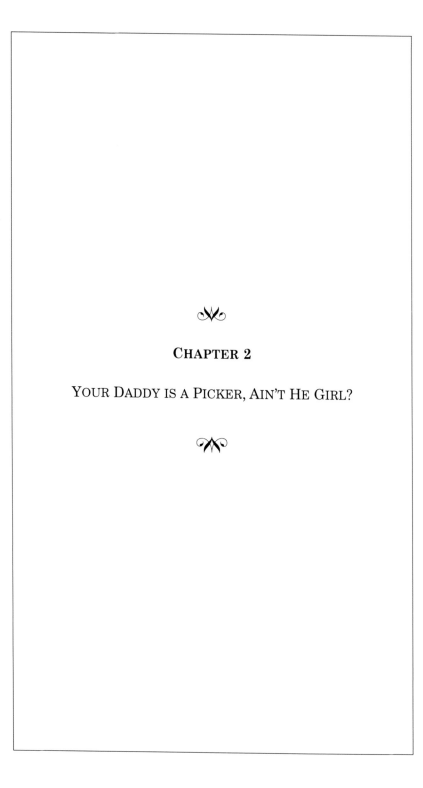

CHAPTER 2

YOUR DADDY IS A PICKER, AIN'T HE GIRL?

YOUR DADDY

Your Daddy is a picker, ain't he girl?
Pickin guitar with that bluegrass band?

Not my daddy. My daddy's not a picker.
You mighta heard him though-
Singin in the Church of God choir.

You shoulda seen your daddy
When he was settin St. Louis on fire.
Him and Lee struttin down the street
So full of themselves,
The sidewalk hardly big enough to hold em.

Not my daddy-
My daddy's lovin my mama
And he's singin in the Church of God choir.

Your daddy's getting strange, youngin.
Weird, not wanting to go with us no more.
Stayin home and gettin bored.

Not my daddy, he's not bored,
He quit swaggerin out the swingin door.
My daddy's lovin my mama,
And he's singin in the Church of God choir.

Your daddy's found the Lord, ain't he child?

THAT's my daddy.
He quit swaggerin out the swingin door.
My daddy is lovin my mama
And he's singin in the Church of God choir.

– Patricia Robert

THE BABY OF THE FAMILY

I have the distinct and dubious honor of being "the baby of the family." To those of you who are perhaps the eldest or the middle child, this may cause a sneer to curl your lip. Yes, we babies have been coddled, favored, pampered, and...well, *babied* to the point of causing resentment and dissention among our siblings. I, myself, have never had a problem with it. The only thing I didn't like about being the baby is that my mother never failed to introduce me as "Geriann–our baby of the family." No matter how many times I rolled my eyes or said "Mom, will you please stop calling me that?" it never made any difference. Up until Mom passed away when I was 35, she still introduced me as her baby.

Being the baby of the family had its advantages. I was the last of a brood of five in our farm family, so Mom held me back in the house and I only occasionally had to help bale hay, drive a tractor, or weed the bean field. Instead, I learned the finer things in life such as helping to cook and wash dishes from four meals a day for a pack of hungry, older siblings, the last meal sometimes as late as 10:00 at night. Collecting eggs, which required fending off sadistic chickens, and picking vegetables from the snake and spider infested garden were also my assigned duties. Then there was the ironing of important items such as pillowcases and my dad's work handkerchiefs (why those shouldn't have wrinkles, I never knew).

Maybe my dad never forced the issue of my helping outside, having seen the look of terror on my face the few times he needed me to drive the tractor. Then there were the times when the cows would get out and he'd make me stand at a large gap between the bushes in the dead of night with thunder booming and the sky streaked with lightning. He would yell to me, "If the cows try to get through here, wave your arms, stomp your feet and yell real loud!" I was never so scared in all of my seven years. I would gladly have ironed a million handkerchiefs and pillowcases to be anywhere else but in the path of stampeding Holsteins. This is not one of my happier memories.

A better memory of being the baby of the family is Christmastime. In my house, Santa always came to my living room on Christmas Eve night. Sometime in the early evening while one of my brothers was driving my sister and me around to look at the neighbors' Christmas lights, Santa would come to our living room. When we got home, we knew if he had come because the living room door off the kitchen would be closed.

We'd eat a hasty meal once Dad and the boys came in from milking, then it would be time to line up by the door, youngest to oldest. No peeking through the keyhole, though, or as Mom assured me, Santa would blow pepper on your eyeball. Thinking about it now, Santa was kind of twisted back then.

Mom would then enter the living room through another doorway and give the "all clear" sign that it was ok to come in, that Santa was gone (as well as the threat of pepper in my eyeball). I'd gently turn the doorknob and swing it wide open, savoring the gradual eyeful of amazing treasures. My memories of these magical moments are documented in the old home movies that Mom would take, as she stood waiting for us in the living room. With her movie camera and blinding bright lights, she tried to capture our expressions as we saw our hearts' desires laid out before us. Santa didn't believe in wrapping paper so we were able to see everything at once. In my childlike memory, I seemed to move in slow motion while discovering the several items, holding them in awe, and then unboxing them to play with. My older brothers were getting things that I couldn't care less about, so I would be lost in my own little piece of heaven–except to say, "Mommy, look! Look what Santa brought me!" She would smile and say, "Yes, you must have been a very good girl," the happiness on her face, a reflection of all our faces. All of her planning, saving and cajoling Dad for just a bit more money for Christmas had paid off.

After everyone had a chance to look through their gifts and Mom was done getting hugs of thanks from the older kids and hugs of happiness from me, she would pour us each a cup of eggnog. We would sit in our cozy living room drinking eggnog, munching peanut brittle and other assorted Christmas candies, and listening to carols sung by Perry Como and Andy Williams. The aluminum Christmas tree in the corner slowly turned a rich red, royal blue, golden yellow and bright orange from the spinning, oscillating wheel plugged in nearby. I would be nestled in Mom's lap getting sleepy from all of the excitement of the evening and the next thing I knew, I'd wake up in bed the next morning with my new doll in my arms. Being the baby and falling asleep first was never an issue. There were always three teenaged brothers or Dad available to carry me upstairs to bed. If the truth were known, I wasn't always completely asleep. There's something to be said for the sensation of having strong arms gently lifting, carrying and tucking you into bed.

These are just a few of my memories of being the baby. My siblings might put a different slant on these same events, but it doesn't matter–they're my memories, and after all, I'm the Baby.

– *Geriann Fitzgerald*

ENDINGS...THEN BEGINNINGS

There was a day
When my son and I were very close, yet
I'd get frustrated over little things and yell
"Shut that refrigerator door!" or complain
About chores not done, or mud on the floor

There was a day
When so many things changed in our home
As he grew older and chose to live on his own
Now he doesn't annoy me with dirt on his shoes
My floors are clean but the house seems empty

There was a day
When I wondered if I would ever adjust
To our lives ending - as they had been
No special surprise hugs from behind
Or laughing about silly things with him

There was a day
When my son brought home the girl
Of his dreams...they decided to share their lives
But there was a happy ending for me; now I realize
There can't be new beginnings without endings

Today is the day
I am excited to say, that my son
Became a father; now I know a thrill
So incredible, it makes me tremble
I am holding their newborn baby girl!

Happy birth day, Rosalee!

– Donna Schenk

RED, BLUE AND NOT WHITE

The law of supply and demand is second nature among even the youngest members of large families. Before I was five years old, I sensed that if I revealed my criteria for choosing pictures in coloring books, the demand for the good pictures would increase among the other colorers who would then color them all up. The good pictures were rare enough as it was, especially at my grandmother's where, upon my occasional visits I would color in books I shared with her sixteen other grandchildren who colored during their occasional visits.

My grandmother sat nearby as I flipped through pages thick with the work of my cousins. She mused over each page I tapped, and in her high-pitched half voice proclaimed the artist behind each work. "Danny colored that one; he likes airplanes. Linda or Susan did that one, I'm not sure. I think Jimmy colored that one; he stays inside the lines pretty well."

I chose a picture to color. In silence, she watched as I ran my hands through the well-used crayons in the old cigar box, searching for any little crumb of the color. Just as my frustration had nearly foreclosed my interest in coloring, from her apron pocket came a red crayon. She knew. I spent a quick second wondering how she knew. Then I dropped the pretense, grabbed the red crayon and colored away.

I loved red. I loved my brother's red bedspread with its cowboys, lassoes, lariats and bucking broncos. Red food tasted the best: beets, tomatoes, red apples, and cherries. For me, it was red popsicles or none. I loved the red Koolaid my grandmother served along with the butter cookies I dipped right in the Koolaid so they would be red as well. I had red shoes and snow boots, a red umbrella, a red and black cow-girl outfit, and a plaid flannel-lined red jacket.

Red fell to the wayside after I started first grade at St. Ambrose where I learned that red was for loose women. The nuns pushed blue, the color of the Blessed Virgin. I could not see blue very well. Not until

I was much older, for example, did I appreciate the often remarked-on pure, crystalline blue of my grandmother's half-moon eyes.

Much about my grandmother escaped me then: her Irish accent; her silent tolerance of the antics of my gruff, cantankerous grandfather, Sam; how she kept to herself behind the swinging kitchen door when her brothers visited. She was especially reclusive around the youngest, the Monsignor, who played piano for the rest of the family out in the parlor. I took for granted her daily attendance at mass at St. Ambrose, kneeling in the last pew, rosary dangling from hand, even though none of my school mates were similarly subject to such surveillance by an elder relative. I was probably 18 years old before I recognized her in the photos on her buffet in which she was a very tall, very thin, pug nosed, sweet faced young lady at home in Fourth of July Hollow with her parents and brothers. The photos show her laughing, playing and clowning with her handsome brothers. Her brothers all called her Annie, even though her first name was Bridget.

On rare occasions I slept over at my grandparents' house during summers and I observed Bridget go through her morning routine. She moved quickly through brushing out her thin grey waist-length hair which she twisted up into a coil on top of her head, securing the roll with large amber pins. Invariably she donned a blue print or checked cotton shirt-waist dress, seamed nylon stockings and black baby-doll pumps that reminded me of my dance teacher's tap shoes. Then she fixed breakfast for Sam and me before bolting out the door to get to mass.

It was while I was away at college that Sam wound up in a nursing home. My mother and my aunts took turns driving Bridget there each day to feed Sam; he would not eat without her. She tended to him daily even while she was undergoing treatment for cancer. The children refused to tell Sam when Bridget died. He ranted and raved about her absence. And then he went silent, refused to eat and finally died four weeks after Bridget's funeral. After Sam's funeral, I lingered with my parents, aunts, uncles, cousins, and her lone surviving brother, the Monsignor, who had said the funeral mass. We were gathered at their two-story stone home which Sam had built shortly after he and Bridget were married. Out came the photo albums and I worked at committing to memory the names of the faces captured.

Monsignor said Bridget had loved to dance and used to do so at every opportunity, then all who could remember joined in on the topic, smiling at the thought, and a couple of my aunts even imitated her which made us all laugh. They worked hard to convince the grandchildren that the quiet, prayerful, penitent grandmother we knew had once enjoyed a life far different from the one we had witnessed. Her hair was raven black, said Monsignor. And she was especially beautiful when she wore red. She loved red.

In Bridget and Sam's thirty-fifth wedding anniversary picture, a very thin Bridget is wearing a black and white dress with a black patent-leather belt. My grandfather is smiling and the couple is surrounded by five of their six children. My father, Michael, their oldest, is absent. I recall from long ago my mother explaining to her friend that the newspaper announcement of the anniversary party included the wedding date which was a short five months before my father was born. "Mike went hunting that day. He was ashamed. Well, you know she had those six big brothers, and I understand they pretty much strong-armed Sam into converting so she could marry him. He didn't want to. . ."

In her wedding picture, my grandmother at age 28 is stylish in flapper-era apparel. The photo is in black and grey. Her dress is not white.

– Elizabeth Parker

5ᵗʰ Honorable Mention
2004 Saturday Writer's Short Story Contest

CONNECTING THE DOTS

Sunset so beautiful,
    Sunset so rare,
Remember the evening
    We grasped its reality?

Clouds showing purple
    Against an orange sky–
Light glinting gently, illuminating shafts of ocean
    And playing peek-a-boo with trees.

Twilight in an ocean-side churchyard,
    This evening of amethyst splendor...
Many may view this scene,
    The orange and purple dancing shadows.

But they cannot have our sunset,
    This time of magic and peace.
Finding their own can take
    A lifetime of sharing.

This magnificence surpasses the eye
    And reaches straight in our hearts–
Delighting in the moment
    And connecting the dots of our hearts

Connected by love and beauty––
    My family, the sunset, and I.

– Patricia Robert

THE FIRST BIRTHDAY

Today I came across a picture of my son Kevin's first birthday party. It's a picture of him standing on one of our dining room chairs in our first home in St. Louis. He is leaning over a cake with his big brother Sean beside him. With equal parts of wind and spit, they managed together to blow out the one big candle and the picture shows his bemusement at where the fire might have gone. This photo is especially endearing to me when I look at their little round cheeks and intent brown eyes gazing at the clown cake that only a moment ago had been on fire. I can almost hear Sean in his too-cute, four-year-old voice saying, "Way to go, Kevvie!!!" and I can hear Caveman Kevin's reply of "Ugh!" Kevin was an early walker, but not an early talker.

In the picture, Kevin has a big red scrape and bruise on the top of his head from walking past the swing set earlier that day while someone was swinging. He had started walking at nine months, much to my dismay, as common sense is in short supply in tots so young. I remember picking him up while he screamed, and praying he was ok. There wasn't any blood, but it was a good clip and I worried about a concussion. But Kevin was made of sterner stuff. There was a reason we called him the Kevinator.

All around that table stood cousins, aunts, uncles, and grandparents singing "Happy Birthday." From the Fitzgerald side would come the finale of "CHA CHA CHA CHICKEN NOODLE SOUP!!!" My side of the family would always smile curiously at this strange tradition of theirs, but learned to tolerate it well.

Once the cake was cut, I had put Kevin in his high chair with a piece of cake to eat all by himself. Much more cake landed on his face and high chair than what had actually made it into his mouth. He still loves cake with a passion. I'm just glad he uses a fork now and not his fists.

Back then, as a relatively new mom, I had no clue the multitude of joys, smiles and wonders that awaited me. My boys had already been such a source of fun; I couldn't imagine it getting any better. Years later, when my growing boys gaze down on me and wrap their octopus-like arms around me, I think back to when I held them then–how they each curled into me, laying their head on my shoulder, and my body would gently sway, rocking them deep into my heart.

– Geriann Fitzgerald

MY DAUGHTER

Where did you come from?

I've asked you that so many times. Once you told me "the zoo". I think you were three then.

Through the years, I've watched you grow, remembering clearly the first time we knew you were on your way. We ran out and picked up baby shoes and miniature socks that could fit on my thumb. We didn't even know if you were a boy or a girl. We didn't care; we knew you would be ours.

Then your day arrived.

"It's a girl," we heard the doctor say. And there you were. Your tiny cries were like music to our ears. Your skin was so pink and your crystal clear eyes such a vibrant blue. We took you home on that hot July day and you became a part of us forever.

But where did you come from?

I've watched you grow from a delicate soft baby into a tiny toddler, your arms and legs trying desperately to hold you steady as you learned to become more steadfast in your ways. I watched your golden hair grow long and saw gentle breezes lift it up to catch the rays of the sun while you played in the grass. I listened to you as you laughed and learned to sing and to dance.

I've watched you because a movie, a play or a Broadway show could never be more captivating or entertaining. Your love of life, your enthusiasm, the way you light up a room, your smile, the sound of your voice; I hear it all, I see it all and I feel it all.

I've watched you evolve into a beautiful child with your own opinions, thoughts and dreams. You are an individual, growing up strong and secure. But in you I also see glimpses of each of your Grandpas and Grandmas, and your Dad...and me. I am honored to be your mother.

You are not only my daughter, but also my friend. I see who you are and imagine the magnificence, the magic and the wonder of who you will become. I see you. I hear you. I love you.

But where did you come from?

I will tell you. You came from my soul.

– Meg Bergmann-Danielle's mom

January 2005

MAKING SOUP ON SATURDAY AFTERNOONS

In my mind, nothing compares with making soup on a Saturday afternoon. It's not only the soup making, it's the whole Saturday thing. A perfect Saturday is a day when I have nowhere I have to be other than home, and I'm not on any time schedule. All I have to do is the laundry, make some soup, be with my family and address a dozen other minor details that I try to do, but if they don't get done, that's ok too.

Ideally, I rise at 6 or 7 on a Saturday morning. I enjoy sitting at my kitchen table with a steaming hot cup of coffee watching the sun rise, or if it's mild enough, on our screened-in porch drinking coffee with my husband. We use this time to get reacquainted and hash over the past week and discuss the upcoming one. We talk about the kids, how we think they're doing: their strengths, weaknesses, what we're doing right, what we need to do differently. It sounds pretty serious, but it's not really, and we've got it down to a science. After about an hour of heart-to-heart, it's time to get moving. "Wastin' daylight!" I say aloud to no one in particular. Possibly the caffeine from my two mega-mugs of coffee has something to do with my abundant energy.

I prefer to save most of the laundry until Saturday and then do all nine or ten loads of it. Once I've sorted it and put the first load in, I set the table for breakfast. My husband cooks fabulous breakfasts, so I let him. I've managed to avoid learning to cook the perfect breakfast for years (at least when my husband is around). When I've been an especially charming wife (and if we happen to have green pepper and mushrooms in the house), he makes me the most awesome ham, cheese and veggie omelet. Then it's on to paying bills, changing bed linen and several other minor, but important details--all the while switching loads and folding clothes.

My kids' favorite soup is a recipe my mother-in-law gave me for ham and bean soup. Once I start sautéing the onions and garlic, the whole house knows what I'm up to. Suddenly, I'm the best mom in the world. I feel such a warm contentment being in my kitchen with a fragrant pot of soup bubbling on the stove. Meanwhile, I sit at the kitchen table folding little boxers and big boxers, trying to match socks and marveling at how big they've gotten. The kids buzz through, sometimes with friends, stopping to stir and sniff the soup. They take a moment to talk, crack me up, and allow a spontaneous hug. I can't explain why all of this makes me happy, but it does. These Saturdays happen infrequently enough that I don't take them for granted, and often enough that I know, most assuredly, that life is good.

– Geriann Fitzgerald

FISSION

Sage of the times and
masters failed before you.
And you will never know
all that you have bested
with your explosive power.

With no more effort than
a blink of your eyes or
a stretch and a yawn, you
taught her who she is and
of her awesome powers.

You, her North Pole,
have set her on her path.
You walk it with her always;
you fuel her journey and
implode her dams of fear.

You, her North Star,
diminutive spark
in sweet oblivion
sleeping in her arms,
are one year old today.

– Elizabeth Parker

PAPA

One might have called Papa an uneducated man. What else could one think when it was learned he never went to school? Ah, but he could fool you. He had never been inside a classroom, yet he knew his numbers. All his bills were paid on time. He knew when the taxes were due. He was honest, and respectful, and a very good neighbor.

Ask him who was president of the United States, and he could tell you. He knew when the price of bread, or the price of pipe tobacco, went up. Year after year, his vegetable garden was the most prized in the neighborhood. It belonged on a garden tour.

Papa grew up over a century ago on his family farm in southern Italy, as close to the dirt as an earthworm. His boyhood home was in a poor mountainous region, where it was always insufferably hot and dry, always lacking enough water, always a land of hard work. Farmers barely squeezed out a living. Traveling was done on the back of a burro.

Papa never went to school, but he learned when to prune the grapevines. He knew the right time to plant peppers, the right time to water the fig trees and lemon trees. He could shake the trunks in a whole grove of ancient olive trees and get every last ripe olive to fall. All this without ever having done one night of homework for school.

That wasn't all. He learned how to press the olives into rich oil. For holiday feasts he could butcher a hog in the morning and have the chops ready for dinner. He could fire up the outdoor oven for his mother to bake her large, round loaves of bread. Papa could get an ornery burro moving again. Farm animals were part of his family.

As a young boy, his muscles grew as he hauled water from a deep well, a daily ritual. His handsome, dark face featured a strong, angular jaw. Bushy eyebrows framed those brilliant brown eyes. There was that mischievous half-smile he carried with him all his life. Thick, black hair, wavy and unmanageable, often fell over his forehead in wet curls. In his youth he must have been irresistible.

He made the voyage to America in 1913, when he was twenty. The trip was made in search of an easier way to make a living. His brother came with him. Their goal was to find good jobs, make money, and send it back to the "Old Country" so the rest of the family could join them in America. But that didn't happen. In the end, it was only the two brothers who came and stayed in "The Land of Opportunity." Papa settled in Milwaukee to make his fortune in the country whose streets were "lined with gold."

The new immigrant also wanted to find a wife and start a family. He was introduced to Mama by a fellow worker and fell in love at first sight. She was an immigrant too, having arrived in America in 1920 with her two sisters and a young brother, under the guidance of their uncle. When she met Papa, she was working as a seamstress in a tailor shop, a job she gave up to get married and tend to her growing family.

In the beginning, my father dug ditches to bury gas lines, a strenuous job he gave up because his boss didn't want him smoking a pipe on the job. "Tony!" the boss would thunder. "You can't smoke on the job! Do you want to blow us all up?"

But Papa had his priorities. His corncob pipe, one of the few pleasures of life, came first. He found another job at a steel foundry. He worked the night shift because it paid more. The position was a step up for him, and he stayed with it for the next thirty-three years until his retirement.

After Papa was married, the babies came often; eight of us lived, and two died in infancy. I was the second oldest. There were five daughters and three sons. My parents discovered it was not easy raising children during the Great Depression, when almost everyone was poor.

Times were tough, and although Papa kept his foundry job, he made only $7 a week. Not much to support a family of ten. Unable to keep up payments, he lost the house he had bought with hard-earned savings. The new owners let him stay as a renter, but it meant coming up with $29 for rent every month. For extra income, he sharpened knives and scissors for neighborhood housewives.

On weekends he filled balloons with helium and sold them at South Shore Beach near Lake Michigan. When he came home after a successful stint at the beach with his pockets full of nickels, we thought he was the richest man in the world. Best of all, we kids each got a nickel for an ice cream cone. What a treat!

To save on expenses, Papa would often be found in the basement cutting and nailing leather soles on our worn-out shoes. The rubber heels he would buy at the dime store, but the soles he carved out from a piece of leather he bought at the tanning factory.

In the end, in spite of all the efforts Papa made to support the family, he needed help from the county. No financial help was available, only commodities. I often rode in the coaster wagon Papa used when he collected his twice-monthly allotment of food, all of which was canned or dried. There was nothing fresh. Mama didn't want anyone to know they were "on the county." She was too proud to go to the food depot. She made Papa do the dirty work.

We didn't know it at the time, but those bags of farina, cocoa, raisins, oatmeal, prunes, flour, split peas, and rice offered us an extremely healthy diet. From the canned milk we enjoyed the best of puddings, and sister Marge often made really good fudge.

Everything fresh came from Papa's bountiful vegetable garden, grown on a small city lot. Mama could make a hearty meal with a dime's worth of neckbones, or a nickel's worth of brick cheese or boiled ham. Eggs were a penny apiece, so there were omelets in every form. We didn't know what junk food was. The only time we ever got soda pop was at a wedding or the yearly company picnic. A real treat was getting a bottle of homemade root beer from our neighbors, who made it in their cellar.

Meanwhile, Papa kept working at the foundry. It was torturous work, especially during those humid Milwaukee summers, when heat from furnaces that melted the ore almost melted the workers. Accidents were frequent. Mama kept an old sheet she cut up in strips and used for bandages. Often Papa had his burns wrapped up with the white pieces of cloth. His work clothes were always full of small burn holes that Mama tried to keep patched. Even after he bathed, he still smelled like the foundry.

On sultry summer weekends Papa would take off his shirt to keep cool. When he strolled around the house in his undershirt, Mama would scold him. "Tony, can't you see your daughters are in the room? Put your shirt back on!" Mama, always prim and proper, had the last word on propriety in our household.

As a girl, I recall staring at Papa's thick arms, and how the veins roped around them like a healthy vine. It would make him laugh when I traced the raised veins with my small fingers. His huge, callused hands were the hands of a man who knew the world of work. They could fix any of life's problems.

Those callused hands picked us up to sit on his shoulders so we could see the Fourth of July parade better. Those powerful hands and all the tasks they performed kept our family going. I would look at his hands and feel safe. And I wonder, did I ever thank him for all the times he sharpened my school pencils with his pocketknife? In my mind he was the best pencil sharpener of all.

How hard it must have been for him to get some sleep with eight noisy youngsters in the family. As we left for school in the morning, there was Papa at the breakfast table, just home from work, tired, dirty, heaving a sigh, like a migrating bird reaching its destination. Mama always had a huge breakfast waiting for him to erase the fatigue.

We didn't see much of our father during our growing-up years. It seemed he was always working or sleeping. Because he had the night shift, he slept most of the day. When school was out in summer, it was especially hard for us to keep quiet while he tried to get some sleep.

But on weekends, his half-smile would turn into laughter as he watched us play in the back yard, or in the alley behind the house. We would play hopscotch, skip rope, play hide and seek, or kick the can. He sometimes played checkers with us.

He often watched me play marbles with my friends, and even dug the holes for us to shoot our marbles into. He didn't say so, but I think he was inwardly proud of the stash of marbles I had won. I kept them in an old pillowcase. When his friends came to visit, he would take them to our closet and, with a happy grin, show them the bulging pillowcase.

Papa took us for walks to Lake Michigan, three miles away, and sometimes we fished for yellow perch off Government Pier. We often walked to the city's outskirts to help him pick newly sprouted dandelion greens for salad. He knew exactly when and where to find the choicest leaves. He certainly enjoyed the way Mama fixed those greens, dressed in vinegar and olive oil.

Since my father never owned a car, he never learned to drive. "Why do I need a car when I have two good legs?" he would say. He walked everywhere, a fact that no doubt contributed to his extraordinary good health and longevity. He walked to work, walked to the store to buy his pipe tobacco, and walked to the farmer's market to buy Concord grapes to make wine in his basement.

Papa was famous throughout the neighborhood for his homemade vino. That half-smile grew into a sheepish grin whenever someone complimented him. Not many knew he had worked in the vineyards of Italy since he was a toddler. The old winepress he used is still stored in my sister Marge's basement. We couldn't bear to get rid of it after he died.

Papa lived to be ninety. Like a life-long security blanket, he was always there for me. Now, years later, and out of nowhere, visions of Papa descend on me. I see him in our basement filling up the copper kettle with water on wash days, then carrying the heavy container to the stove to heat. I picture him stringing up wash lines in the backyard for Mama to hang up her laundry. I can see him lighting up his corncob pipe, or firing up our pot-bellied stove with coal to keep us warm in winter.

And there he is on the porch, early on a summer morning, scanning the sky and checking the weather. Would it rain, or did he need to water the eggplants today? Time and again he put educated weather forecasters to shame with his correct predictions. All of this happened without his ever having walked through the doors of a school house.

I visualize him wiping up the last bit of spaghetti sauce on his plate with a piece of Mama's homemade bread. And there is Papa, going down the basement steps carrying a bushel of tomatoes for Mama to can. I picture him shoveling snow off the sidewalks. Whenever I pick up a pencil, I see Papa sharpening it to a fine point. He is always with me. When I think of him, it feels like a bird is flapping its wings within my chest. It's a happy, secret feeling, knowing that this silent hero, this uneducated man, was my very own smart Papa.

– Lucy Engbring

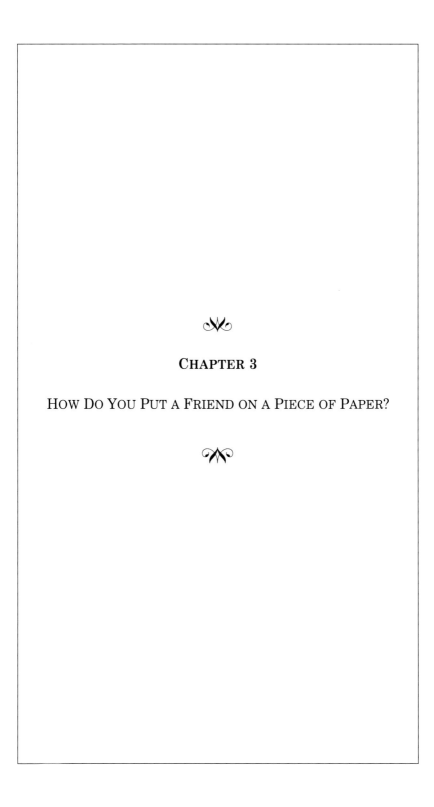

CHAPTER 3

HOW DO YOU PUT A FRIEND ON A PIECE OF PAPER?

MY TREE

A proud tall evergreen stands alone silhouetted against the sky at the edge of an immense field. A few dark green branches cling close to the base of its sturdy central trunk. Above them, widely spaced dark bare branches fan out and upward, holding their burden of needled foliage near their tips. The sky can be seen through them. The wind and birds play among the branches. The tree reaches out further as it goes higher, and is topped with an arch of sunlit green.

It has always been my tree, my landmark as I traveled the Valmeyer Road these many years. How does it come to be here? It is like no other tree in the area. Was there once a homestead on this spot? Every time I pass by it I silently thank the farmer who for years has carefully cultivated around it.

I remember seeing it in the spring, when the field was the bright green of freshly sprouting winter wheat, in summer when the wheat turned to gold and Queen Anne's Lace frothed the roadway. I remember autumn, when it wore its green with dignity, refusing to conform to the red and gold fashions displayed by other trees on the far distant horizon. In winter it stood in a field of pristine white, its branches trimmed with ermine.

I remember a late trip home from a night meeting in Valmeyer. A violent thunderstorm was raging. Sheets of rain clouded my windshield. Wind whipped against my car, making it swerve alarmingly. Lightening zigzagged across the sky. In its bright light I saw, to my left, my tree, standing sturdy and tall and unafraid. Its strength reassured me, and I made it home safely.

This summer I took a morning to sit on the side road and paint my tree. The breeze that came up made the sound of the ocean in its high branches, and wafted a piney fragrance to me. I worked all morning, unaware of the traffic that whizzed by. It was a labor of love, but how do you put a friend on a piece of paper? I really don't need to, because it will always be a part of me, my beautiful majestic, lonely tree.

– Elizabeth Hoffman

SAM

He is a sad and sickly sight, in disgrace with all the neighbors. Their flowerbeds are suffering from his bathroom habits, since he doesn't favor his own. But this mangy dog doesn't show hard feelings when yelled at by these offended parties. His slow departure and wagging tail are sure signs of that.

His name is Sam and he is an unidentifiable mixture of breeds. This old and stiff canine was never an Adonis but has lost whatever good looks he once might have had. Wise brown eyes peek through the tangled fur. If the eyes are the windows to the soul, his inner substance must be more complex than most humans'.

His rheumatic body never fails to rise from the ground to greet the members of his home, and the lack of response is not an issue to him. The occasional escort of the family car out of the subdivision is becoming a stressful journey, but he is not ready to give this up.

Our Sam has a moment of glory when the school bus visits the corner of his street. His bony body strains as he attempts a galloping motion. It is the happiest and fastest action he is capable of. While the small students tumble from the bus, the dog grins in anticipation. They surround him and their small hands enter the warm, brown fur. He stands motionless, only his tail and liquid brown eyes are moving, like a statue surrounded by backpacks and their owners.

On the way home his body is moving much slower, but his tail is still wagging.

– Gea Pierce

Neighborly Love

Many are inspired by mentors, special people
that leave lasting impressions; I learned
valuable life-lessons from a nurturing neighbor

I thought that she would be lonely, instead
she filled her home with lovely melodies on the piano
and the myriad of songbirds kept her company

She would stop in mid-conversation
to listen to their sweet song, then inform if it was
a wren, sparrow, oriole, or cardinal singing

The porch swing creaked as I watched her crochet
while her rocker kept a soothing rhythm with her needle
It appeared she enjoyed her own company, too

Her pace was rarely hurried, and she was unable
to simply pass by the wildflowers winding up
the weathered picket fence that divided our backyards

With delight in her eyes, she would stop
amazed at the blending colors, or stand and quietly gaze
as if it were the first time she had ever discovered them

So gently, she would touch the feathery petals
of the fragrant flowers, as a mother would
tenderly stroke her newborn infant's fingers

She included me, no matter how much she had to do
and always took time to give thanks...in awe of her amaryllis,
spring's perennial surprises or for the awaited rain

A life lived so simply, yet always filled
with a sense of wonder, but most of all
it was the gift of her love that altered my life

This amazing lady not only taught me that I, too
had special gifts - but more, she helped
me learn that I *was* a special gift

– *Donna Schenk*

In Loving Memory of Pearl Hartmann
1904-2004

AS WE HELD HANDS

In Loving Memory of Leona

From an awkward beginning
"Lord, please bond us"
To sharing laughs as well as fears
And as we remembered pasts
We shed tears...
As we held hands

I watched you grow from bitter to sweet
Your eyes brightened, as I sat and listened
The verse "We were weaved together
By threads of gold" revealed the depth
Of our connection...
As we held hands

An early morning call came with a shock
Whispered fears left us helpless
What could I do?
I wet your lips, gave you sips
You warmed my heart, gave me joy...
As we held hands

One last laugh, "Bubba ate the scarecrow"
You didn't want me to leave
I didn't want you to go
So we sat a little closer
Squeezed a little tighter...
As we held hands

One last hug from heaven
Then words were not necessary
What was said was not spoken
A bond of love
And devotion...
As we held hands

– Donna Schenk

*A tribute to those who reach out to the aged
and alone in nursing homes*

MY FRIEND DEREK

The plane was late. Very late. I was at the St. Louis Airport waiting to board a flight to Phoenix. My frame of mind was beginning to match the stormy darkness outdoors. Rain was drumming against the wide windows. Arcs of lightning jabbed at the runways.

The loudspeaker announcement blamed the flight delay on the thunderstorms, as though we couldn't see that for ourselves. I noticed other passengers waiting with me at Gate 18 were getting restless too.

Suddenly, another announcement crackled through the air. Would passengers be willing to board a different flight to our destination? The two hours of waiting quickly came to an end as almost all of us agreed to board anything that would fly.

The unexpected change of plans gave me three hours and ten minutes of the most delightful visit I've ever experienced on a plane. Plopping down in the seat next to me was a lively, blond 12-year-old boy who radiated energy. Even before he had his seat belt fastened, he said, "Hi. Are you going to Phoenix? You are? Me too!"

Anyone who travels knows how it is with those who sit next to you on a plane. You can tell right away who wants to be friendly and talkative, and who wants to be left alone. The loner will immediately open a book or newspaper and start reading, keeping to himself. Or he may lean back in his seat and close his eyes. You get the message.

But not Derek, my friendly pal, a sixth-grader from Indiana who was on his way to the desert to visit his uncle. As soon as he asked if I liked spiders, I knew this was going to be a fun trip. He was a collector.

He heard there were scorpions in Arizona. He had always wanted one for his collection, and he asked if I had ever seen one.

"Yes, I did," I told him. "On one trip to the valley, I was going on a picnic and taking some drinks along. But when I opened the cooler, there was a scorpion inside."

Derek's jaw dropped open. You would have thought he was sitting next to a celebrity. I could have been the First Lady.

He was full of questions. Was it dead? No, it was alive. Did you kill it? Yes. How? Just got a tissue and mashed it. Weren't you scared? No.

How was he to know I had a long and distinguished record of mashing spiders. Chances were, I told him, that he might not see a scorpion because, in all the years I had been going to the desert, that was the only live one I had ever seen.

I learned Derek was traveling with his father, who was sitting behind us on the crowded plane. His 14-year-old sister, a tall, pretty girl, was sitting just across the aisle from us. When I asked if his mother was on this trip, I knew I had hit a soft spot.

Derek haltingly explained that she was too busy, that she decided to skip this trip. But in the end, he told me the real reason she wasn't there. His parents were recently divorced, and this spring break was a special time with his dad.

"Do you want to see my yearbook?" he asked, changing the subject and digging into a used gym bag at his feet. Sure I would. As he flopped through the pages, I learned who his friends were, who he didn't pal around with, who was popular, who was on the track team, and who mouthed off to the teacher and got suspended.

"Here's me," he said, pointing to a cute photo. He explained this was last year's picture, when he was "young." He said this year's picture would be better. As though he could get any cuter.

One girl's picture had a black X penciled across her face. "What happened here?" I asked. Oh, he didn't like her anymore. "But what about this red heart you've got drawn around her picture?" Well, he used to like her, but now she liked someone else. Ah, so it was a story of unrequited love for this good-looking future heartbreaker.

Then, unexpectedly, "Would you like to sign my yearbook?" Those words turned me back into a school kid again. I was remembering some of the endearing comments written in my yearbooks, especially one that said, "May the bluebird of happiness never poop on your doorstep."

"Dear Derek," I wrote. "Good luck in the future, and have fun in Arizona. I hope your spider collection grows. Your friend, Lucy (The lady who sat next to you on the plane.)" For some reason, I wanted him to remember me.

We learned of each other's likes and dislikes. We talked of sports and music and movies. We discussed food after the snacks had been passed out. "Do you want to swap your granola bar for my cheese dip?" he asked.

"Sure," I said. "Why not?"

It reminded me of swapping sandwiches during lunch hour with my girlfriend when we were kids. She liked my mom's homemade bread and grape jam, while I loved her store-bought pumpernickel rye spread with liver sausage.

The intercom crackled with the captain's voice. We were nearing Phoenix and would land shortly. It was hard to believe our flight was almost over. Camelback Mountain and Squaw Peak came into view as we approached Sky Harbor Airport.

I watched as Derek gathered up his things, wanting to soak him up visually. I didn't want the trip to end. As we said goodbye, my new friend gave me a quick hug. I wondered then if his parents had ever had the pleasure of spending three hours and ten minutes with this 12-year-old jewel of a son. It was my gain.

"So long, Derek," I said. And then, remembering that spiders were his passion, I added, "Hope you find a nice big scorpion!"

– Lucy Engbring

KATZE

Opal eyed golden cat
Contented, relaxed
Sure of care
Surrounded by love

Yet so independent
No one tells her
Where to sleep
When to eat

Her own person
Giving warm fuzzy cuddles
Mittened love pats
Just when I need them

– Elizabeth Hoffman

IT ALL STARTED WITH A QUARTER

In 1970 while in fourth grade, I taped a quarter to a list of my hobbies and interests and mailed it to a company that assured me a computer would be used to choose the perfect pen pal for me. That was the best twenty-five cents I ever spent. I was assigned Mary, another fourth grade girl from St. Philip, Indiana, a small town outside of Evansville. Perfect! I was from St. Rose, Illinois, a small town outside of St. Louis, Missouri. Already we had so much in common! From our list of hobbies, the computer must have chosen the common denominator of John Denver. We had both listed him as one of our interests, so I credit him (may he rest in peace) for giving me my best friend.

Mary and I were both into nature, sunsets, and all that John Denver sang about. We would write long, journal-like letters to each other sometimes covering a span of two weeks, using pages and pages of legal paper and loads of postage stamps on the envelopes. We could tell each other our deepest fears and desires, as we knew our secrets were safe with each other. The distance between us acted as a blanket, insulating us and providing a warmth that let us open our minds and hearts to each other. Over the course of 35 years, we must have written hundreds of letters and emails to each other.

When I was in eighth grade, my family and I stopped in St. Philip during a family vacation to finally meet Mary and her family. As luck would have it, our parents became good friends as well. For several summers after that, Mary and I would try to spend a week or two at each other's house. She taught me to play the guitar and we sang and played every John Denver song we knew. I think we sensed even then, that we were blessed with a special friendship.

Mary and I both attended Mater Dei Catholic High School: she in Evansville, Indiana and I in Breese, Illinois. There are only about four Mater Dei High Schools in the entire country. How coincidental is that? I also went to her senior prom with one of her friends, we were maids of honor in each other's weddings, and both of us married men who had children from previous marriages. Then we each had two boys in our own marriages. The fact that our lives often paralleled became just another interesting facet of our unusual friendship.

For several years, when our kids were little, we didn't get together too often, but now that our boys are teenagers, we have been getting together about four times a year. We both work full time in our careers and are well acquainted with the stresses of being working mothers. So to treat ourselves, we meet on a Friday after work, halfway between St. Louis and Evansville, in Mt. Vernon, Illinois, cutting both of our drives down to an hour and a half. Mary and I check into a hotel, ice up the bottle of wine we'll drink later, and head out for some shopping. Eventually, we'll stop and have a long, leisurely dinner and go back to the hotel, get comfortable, drink our wine, and catch up on each other's lives.

As the wine relaxes us and makes us a little tipsy, we alternately laugh, share things we are scared about, shameful of, and what the future might hold for our families. We also reassure each other what fabulous mothers and friends we are.

Eventually we go to sleep, then wake early and feast on a huge Cracker Barrel breakfast with lots of coffee and more conversation. Then it's time for more shopping as we browse, critique, poke fun, spend money and basically turn back the clock. For 24 hours, we remember what it feels like to be girls again. No responsibilities, no "MOM!"–just Mary and me. After several more hours of shopping, we have a late lunch and wind up our visit. We've done all of our favorite things: shop, talk, eat, drink wine, talk, shop and eat! It just doesn't get any better than that. I know our friendship has an unusual history, and people are often amazed by our story, but it's not hard to keep a friendship going that is so precious. Though we are 300 miles apart, we know we are only a phone call away if we need to talk.

After a big hug and promises to email each other soon, we reluctantly say goodbye. We're both anxious to see our families again, and after all, we know we'll be back in just a few months–no matter what. Mary heads east on I-64 and I head west–home to my family whom I appreciate even more after a mere 24 hours away and who loves me enough to give me this gift of time with my best friend.

– Geriann Fitzgerald

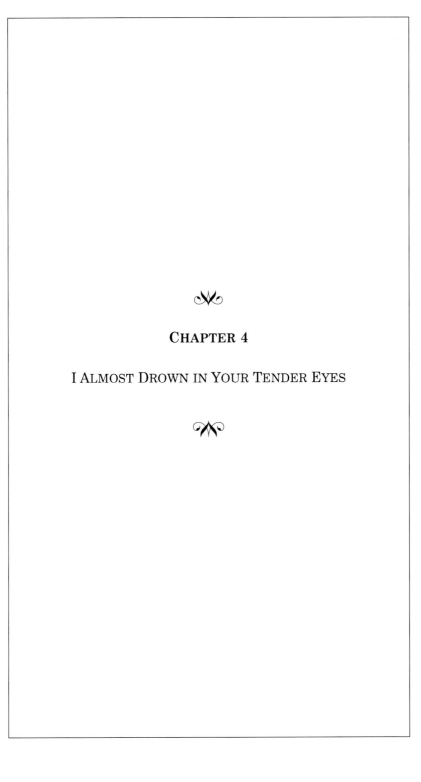

CHAPTER 4

I Almost Drown in Your Tender Eyes

Delicious Love

When the cup touches my lips, the fragrant steam fills me with anticipation. The coffee spreads its warmth through my mouth like a velvet brocade and fills my total being with a deep physical and emotional satisfaction. Your eyes embrace me with a tenderness that makes me quiver, and when our hands meet our fingers curl and hug.

"More coffee?" The waitress speaks softly, not wanting to intrude, while she places the dishes on the table.

"Yes, please," we smile, including her into our world...just for a moment.

You reach for your fork and carefully taste your first fruity bite. I use my fingers to bring my treat to my lips, and my tongue enters the creamy filling, savoring the smooth texture and soft flavor. The outside shell crunches gently, while it blends with the creamy filling against the roof of my mouth. A chocolate sensation combines the strawberry and cream.

We both reach for our cup and our eyes meet, veiled by the steam of our warm brew. You reach over and caress my lips with yours...ever so slightly. With one finger you touch my face and wipe a bit of lost cream from my chin. I reach for my second cannoli, a crisp tube, filled with delightful ricotta. My tongue finds its way to the sweet cream again and I almost drown in your tender eyes.

– Gea Pierce

ALLISON BLUE

I love a man named Allison Blue
But only from a distance

He is the moon to me
Pulling me to him, but only so close

Illuminating something lost in me
Only to turn away

Leaving me, lessening himself to me
But then always returning

Veiled by the sky we see each other
Through a film of wanderlust

Separated by a great expanse
Our long standing romance leaving me blue

Tethered to something that doesn't exist
Shackled by a life imagined

As the pale, placid blue of the daylight sky
Fades to ink and pierces with light

I feel again he's drawing near
Pulling me close, pulling me in

– Melany Nitzsche

RHIZOME

I tell a story
about working the night shift in a hospital nursery,
of dozing while writing in an infant's chart.
On waking, I saw that instead of baby's vital signs,
I had written words to a cheesy pop song
that was playing on a nearby radio.

That story has a parent which I have never told before,
of sitting in front of my mother's house, talking,
giggling at a black kitten dancing
after bugs in moon shadows beneath a tree,
watching lightning bugs blink out their insular rhythm,
recalling encounters we'd had in our neighborhood as kids,
filling each other in on our lives since then,
filling silences with eye talk,
bringing comfort and finding peace,
swearing that we mean it this time when we say
we are not going to see each other again until the weekend,
saying goodnight at 5 a.m.
leaving for school at 8 a.m.
nodding off in shorthand class at 2 p.m.
taking dictation at eighty words per minute while sleeping
and dreaming.

– Elizabeth Parker

WALTZ, WANING

Come with me
to the floor.
      Dance with me.
      Can't you see
          how well we
          make believe
             we're in love?
             With each step
          hand in hand
          you're my girl
      I'm your man.
      We should be
so happy.
Why do I
      sense you're gone?
      Longingly
          right through me
          your green eyes
             don't tell lies.
             There he is -
          your heart's home.
          Soon tonight
      I will be
      with you dear
but I fear
all alone.

– *Melany Nitzsche*

LOVE ON A FIELD ROAD

We teetered down the field road
on the old red four-wheeler.
Milky pink blue clouds glow
as the sun melted into the west.

A cupped moon pouring itself empty
stared down from the glossy sky.
In unison we watched six startled deer
form a crisp line of white flags
and in one fluid leap
they vanished into the brush border.

He leaned his head back to me,
kissed my cheek and softly spoke
you look very beautiful
~ a defining moment.

– Lori Becherer

SUMMER DANCE WITH CORNSTALKS

Blow the dust off this buttermilk moon
and meet me in the fields.
Summer dance with cornstalks spins me
round
      and round
         and round.

Slide your arm behind my back
in a cotton dress with sun-kissed skin.
Find our way around this maize and
twirl
      and twirl
         and twirl.

Cicadas sing for their own reasons;
unaware they share their song with us.
Fireflies circle and dash these rows;
giving our dance floor a bonfire glow.

The world spins slower for us tonight.
This always was our season.
Tassels crown the dimming sky.
Arms encircle me completely.

Harvest seems so far away
at the close of a summer day
as we rise up from the dust
for this summer dance.

– Melany Nitzsche

2nd Place Southwestern Illinois College
2004 Poetry Contest

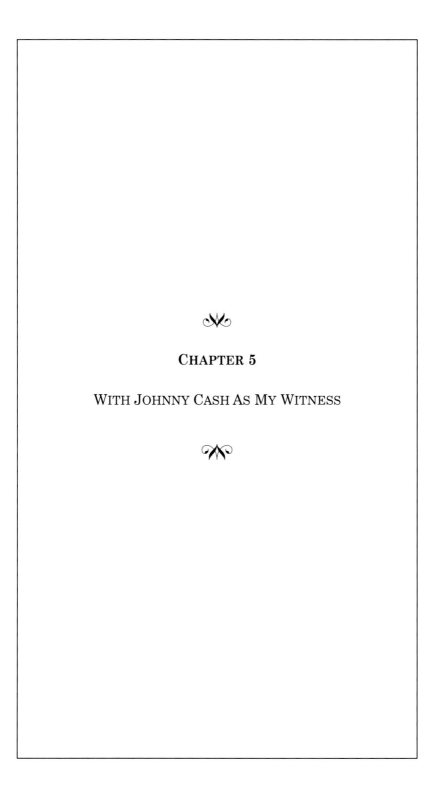

CHAPTER 5

WITH JOHNNY CASH AS MY WITNESS

A SIGHTING AT SUSIE'S

I was surprised to see Elvis eating lunch at Susie's Restaurant in Red Bud last week. Last I heard he was working at a gas station in Wyoming. But I guess if I were a refugee from the world's prying eyes, Red Bud would be just as good a place as any other to hang my hat, or in his case, extra large belt buckle. The people are kind and won't bother you if you don't bother them.

Elvis looks like he is trying a little too hard to hang on to his youth. His hair is still jet black, though I don't think he's fooling anyone regarding its authenticity. According to my calculations, Elvis hit 70 this year. He fixes his hair very fluffy–giving it the illusion of height, width and depth. I am happy to report, however, that he is not wearing jewel-encrusted leisure suits anymore. That would be a little too over the top, certainly blowing his cover and attracting media of the most distasteful variety.

He belts out his conversations with the same enthusiasm he belts out "That's Alright Mama." Apparently, he still likes the spotlight. He is loud and proud. I didn't catch what he was eating for lunch. Maybe he has some sort of special arrangement there regarding fried peanut butter and banana sandwiches. During his meal he keeps craning his head backwards to tell the couple in the booth behind him animated stories. The younger man who accompanied him just smiles and sits back. I can't tell if he's embarrassed or genuinely enjoying being The King's sidekick at lunch.

I must admit, as they were getting ready to leave, I was waiting to see a very theatrical departure. I thought Elvis might acknowledge the crowd with his famous "Thank you very much," complete with lip curl, as if *he* were the special of the day instead of the meatloaf. Maybe time is teaching Elvis modesty. He just smiled and left for his next engagement, perhaps at Heartland Bar & Grill, a little ways down the road. I hear he has quite a following there.

Susie's is a great place to eat even under the most ordinary of circumstances, but dining with near royalty takes the experience to another level. You can imagine my surprise, then, when I went to pay at the register and nearly bumped into Santa Claus as I turned around to leave. There he was, in a grey sweat suit, with his hair pulled into a pony tail. He and his wife had been eating lunch here, too. I guess I had been too absorbed in Elvis to notice the other movers and shakers a mere two booths down from me. As I was leaving my tip at the table, I thought to myself: *That was the most surreal lunch I've ever had.* You can't make that stuff up. It happened just like that, with Johnny Cash as my witness.

– Melany Nitzsche

HEROES CAN DO THAT

Their ages vary, but they are young, very young. The senior in the small group is a two-and-a-half year old boy and the youngest member is a nine-month-old baby boy with large ears and spiky hair. He practices a whimsical, toothless grin.

Another toothless smile adorns the face of a ten-month-old baby girl. She is in the process of endangering the safety of a fourteen-month-old boy who is attempting to crawl across the floor. His chubby little foot is stuck under her walker and he screams, exposing his eight brand-new teeth. The baby girl knows the effect his teeth can have on her fingers; could she be getting even by using her walker? Her blue eyes are wide and innocent. Her curly hair enhances her angelic face. She continues to smile while he screams.

"I'll save you, baby!" Two-and-a-half year old Superman, dressed in hero pajamas, rescues the baby boy from the bad driver in the walker.

"No...I do it!" says an overzealous two-year-old girl. But Superman's little friend is too late. She is the kind of girl who likes to be in charge. He beat her to this rescue and her dark-brown eyes are flashing with anger. She uses her two-year-old power on Superman.

"I'm not your best friend anymore," she pouts with her mouth and her body.

Superman looks defeated. Girl-power outdoes him again. But he is a hero and heroes can handle that.

"Time to eat!" Lunch is ready. They respond quickly to the call of their caretaker.

"Spaghetti, yeah!"

Three toddlers are seated at the table while the older baby joins the feast in the highchair. His eight teeth have graduated him into the finer things of life. An iridescent, sweet smile peeks around his chubby hands and his long lashes quiver as he sucks the succulent noodles from his dimpled fist.

"Babies are messy," announces the senior child while he tries to catch the noodle swinging from the fork above his face. His head follows the pendulum motion of the noodle until he catches it with his orange mouth. Superman has parked his utensil and manages to eat simultaneously with both hands. He raises his orange fists to show his muscles, while sauce drips down his arms. But he is a hero, and heroes can do that.

They clean up in record time and nobody fusses during their diaper-change, because the shoes are waiting and the sun is shining.

It is time to go outside. Another heroic Superman pose, one foot on the soccerball, one hand on his hip. He is filling his diaper.

When the brown-eyed little girl hugs him, she says, "I love you, Superman."

She wrinkles her little nose, and announces, "Superman went poopie."

Ah well. Superman always gets away unscathed! He is a hero, and heroes can do that.

– Gea Pierce

BASTING MY CURTAINS

Basting, *Basting*.
Let's get it straight.
One lays on food
another applied by seamstress.
Or shall you attach
a honey glaze to your curtains
and splash a hem on your turkey?
Let's get it straight
or I shall *beat* you.

Baste: (Merriam Webster's Collegiate Dictionary Tenth Edition)
1) to sew with long loose stitches in order to hold something
   in place temporarily
2) to moisten at intervals with a liquid
3) to beat severely or soundly

– Lori Becherer

DON'T MESS WITH GRANDMA

"Now, will you look at that! She drives a Lincoln and thinks she owns the road!" Her shrill voice made him jump in his seat, bringing him back into the real world. Dave looked at Grandma and noticed her angry mouth pulling her chin closer to her nose.

The offender drove on, not knowing she had provoked the wrong person. She also didn't notice the old Chevy making a U-turn behind her.

"Grandma, please, you promised you would take me to soccer practice." The jaw remained in locked position and her nose made its soft whistling noise. It didn't look good for the lady in the Lincoln or for his soccer practice.

"Grandma, please!" He knew it was a useless attempt to retrieve her from her other world. She had never shared this side of herself with his parents, and Dave was told to quit reading Harry Potter books when he tried to tell them that Grandma had an evil side. The old Chevrolet hiccuped under the abuse and they almost hit the Schwann man's ice-cream truck while they followed their victim through a fast curve.

Dave looked at her squat, powerful legs, clad in pink tights. He had been with her the day she stole those tights at Wal-Mart, along with the tri-color tank top, which showed the butterfly tattoo on the small of her back. She felt his anxious eyes and flashed him an angelic smile. Her eyes sparkled under the fluorescent blue eye shadow, a Famous Barr souvenir. Grandma hummed softly to herself as she parked her car next to the victim's vehicle.

"Ah, Curves," she whispered excitedly, while she watched the lady enter the building to the training room. "I could do that," she said as she pointed to the closing door, "I have enough vinegar left in my old bones."

"Let's go, Grandma, please?"

She looked at him with all the dignity she could muster. "Allow me to remind you that I am not a fan of this child dominated society. I will tell you when I'm ready. You are not in charge here, honey."

Dave made himself small, while Grandma pulled her vertically challenged frame out of the car, dug into her purse and produced a crimson Estee Lauder lipstick. She looked around with a childlike expression on her face, squatted down between the two cars and started "punishing" the offending driver.

When she pulled out her Dillard's silver earring, Dave felt serious concern. He knew it was not a fingernail on a blackboard when he heard the painful sound. Afraid to look, and shrinking further yet into the old car seat, he was well aware of her activities in the parking lot. What if someone left Curves or the Chinese restaurant next door? She would be caught red-handed. It would be embarrassing, yet Mom and Dad would finally have to believe him. Why couldn't she just make cookies like other grandmothers did?

Grinning from ear to ear, Grandma crawled back into the car. Quickly she turned the keys she had left in the ignition. There was only a small scratchy sound. Again, she tried. Nothing! Dave grabbed the door handle. He could hear his own heart beating in fear.

"Where do you think you're going?" she wanted to know.

"Out of here," he muttered in a small voice.

"Don't go anywhere; I have a plan," she said proudly.

He watched her run into Curves, as fast as her short legs could carry her. She almost fell into the door and stood in the doorway panting for air and effect.

"Does anybody here own a silver Lincoln?" Her voice was loud and full of authority. She was followed back to the car by the ladies from Curves and some curious Imo's Pizza customers.

"They were Mexican and had a bowling bag. They kind of looked like that guy." She pointed to the owner of the Chinese restaurant, who was entering the parking lot in his convertible Corvette. Enticed by all the commotion in front of his building, he jumped out of the car, leaving his key in the ignition.

"That man is Oriental," a lanky teenager informed her.

"Same difference," she responded, somewhat irritated.

The onlookers had grown into quite a group by the time the police arrived and Grandma repeated her story with flair, visibly enjoying her performance. Her hands moved like restless birds and her purple contact lenses sparkled with a life of their own.

While all eyes focused on the damaged Lincoln, she slipped into the Corvette and drove away, leaving a speechless audience. Her face was elated in total bliss and Dave knew she would be humming her favorite tune.

– Gea Pierce

SOLILOQUY OF A FITTING ROOM MIRROR

She trudges in to see me
Her hopes high
As she hangs her bargain finds
On dressing room pegs

How brutal I am
How uncaring, how honest
As I reflect
Her many imperfections

Is it my fault that the light
Is unflatteringly bright
That her skin looks pale
Her lipstick garish?

Am I to blame for the bumps and bulges
The sloping shoulders, the aging features
The careless posture
That I reflect on my shiny surface?

Her hostility breaks my heart
As she faces reality, she blames me
But I'm only a dressing room mirror
I've done what I must do

Please wipe the handprints off
Before another hopeful arrives
Perhaps I can give her
A happier report...I'll try

– Elizabeth Hoffman

A New Lease On Life

We like to think we'll live forever. It's a human weakness, one of many, to distance ourselves from anything that might force us to face our own mortality. And yet, one day we may all arrive at the pearly gates of heaven waiting for St. Peter to give us the go-ahead. Once inside, we can compare the size of our angel wings with each other. On the other hand, we could easily end up at the gates of hell wishing for a window fan and a tall glass of ice water.

These thoughts wouldn't have crossed my mind at all except for the phone call my husband Jerry had made to inquire about some auto insurance. He was considering replacing his car and wanted to compare rates. His agent promised to call back with a few quotes.

It wasn't long before the phone rang. The agent said it was the company's policy to check the credit rating of any potential insurance buyer. "Just a matter of form," he said. He was so very sorry to inform my husband that his credit had been denied.

Denied? Did he say denied? Well, a lucky thing my husband was sitting down, because otherwise the news would have floored him. Here was a man who had never missed paying a bill in his life. He was never late, and often paid long before a bill arrived. His taxes were sent in early every year. In other words, he was the perfect customer.

With such a sterling background, why was he denied credit? How could this be? He wanted some answers, and fast. The agent explained that the reason he was denied credit was because he was "Listed as deceased."

Jerry stood up. The vein on his forehead was beginning to pulse. In a rising voice he said, "Tell me, how can I be deceased if I'm right here talking to you on the phone?"

The agent, of course, was not at fault. He was only passing on information the computer had coughed up. In fact, he gave Jerry some helpful phone numbers to call to see if he could get the problem straightened out.

It was too late in the day to make any calls. Dinnertime was over, and most businesses were closed. The matter would have to wait until morning, thus giving Jerry the whole night long to fume about this fiasco.

With a helpless gesture, he turned to me and asked, "How does a person go about proving he's alive? How long will it take to get a computer glitch erased from the system?"

"We'll find out tomorrow," I told him. "Calm down. You can take care of it then. By the way," I teased, "I won't have to make you any dinner tonight. You're supposed to be dead." But I relented and cooked anyway. I had never seen a dead man eat so fast.

The next morning, phone wires sizzled with calls. It was no easy task talking to a recorded voice. Instructions were given to "Punch 1 if you want this," and "Punch 2 if you want that." Papers were to be filled out, copies made of social security numbers, driver's license, bill receipts, and more. Jerry found out it's no fun being dead when you're still alive.

Somehow the mistake was traced back to a business exchange made over a year ago at Christmas time. During the holiday rush the wrong computer keys were punched.

It must have been an easy mistake to make, and a hard one to correct. How and why it all happened remains a mystery to this day. The records still stated, "Listed as deceased."

"That's funny. I don't remember going to your funeral," I told my still seething husband. "Do you know where you're buried, just in case I want to take flowers? Do you like forget-me-nots, or maybe lilacs?"

Jerry was not amused. He muttered under his breath that when the time came, he wanted his ashes scattered over the Mississippi River, or maybe over the backyard vegetable garden.

"No! Not the garden," I told him. I would see his smiling face in every ripe tomato I sank my teeth into. The river would be better. "And how soon would it be," I asked, "before I could collect your life insurance?"

After several days and countless phone calls to set the record straight, my husband was, thankfully, very much alive again. It was like getting a new lease on life. At last he could buy his new car with no worries. Life was good!

Jerry is not yet ready to be fitted with his angel wings. On the other hand, he's drinking plenty of ice water ahead of time, just in case. Now that he is no longer listed as deceased, I think we should celebrate his swift reincarnation. First, let us pause for a moment of silence. After all, I've been sleeping with a dead man for over a week.

– Lucy Engbring

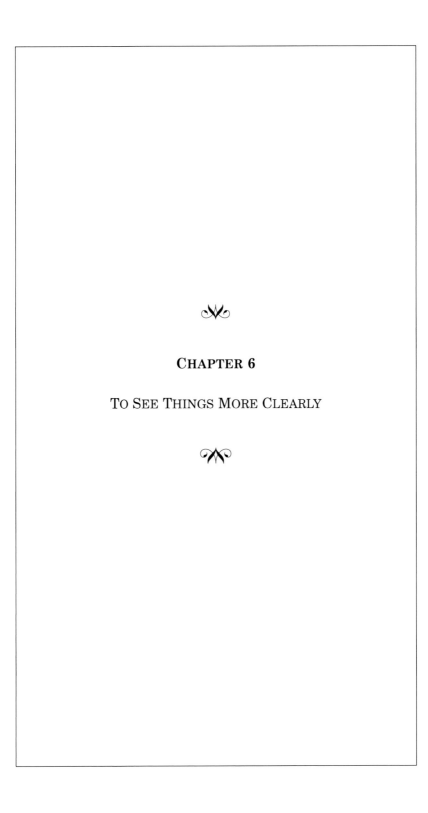

CHAPTER 6

TO SEE THINGS MORE CLEARLY

SOULFUL

Life can get so busy, so full, wecanloseourfocus, so full
That it can be very difficult to see the real meaning or
See our true purpose, with so much pressure to be
Too much to so many. As the blank space that
Separates words in a sentence is essential
So too, are the invaluable times that we
Must have, to slow our pace enough
To find our own *s p a c e* bar
To see things more clearly
A choice - so full or
Soulful, like
Hourglass
Sand
T
i
m
e
is
r
u
n
n
i
n
g
out

– Donna Schenk

WRITING DOWN THE LINES

Sometimes lost in translation
Communication failing
Speech not quite enough
I'm writing down the lines.

Ideas are blurred and faded
Trying to understand opposition
Melting malleable hearts with Love
I'm writing down the lines.

Shreds of torn relationships
Ripped from words and actions past
Mercy hangs in the balance
I'm writing down the lines.

Attempts are made at solace
Sloughing platitudes
And praying to make a difference
I'm writing down the lines.

– Patricia Robert

BEAUTIFUL SCARS

Recently while working out at the gym, I caught my reflection in the floor-to-ceiling mirror. In the reflection, I saw a fortyish looking woman with mussed hair and flushed, damp skin who was visibly struggling to lift mere 20-pound weights. Were these really the same arms that once lifted and vaulted toddlers to the sky? My eyes traveled downward finding faults and places in need of improvements, until they reached my left knee where they lit on a one inch whitish scar that is still visible after more than 30 years. I stared at it for a while, remembering how I got the scar.

It was during recess on a warm spring day, one of the first of the year where life feels good and is begging to be celebrated. I remember being 10 or 11 and daring one of my classmates to race me. I ran effortlessly, as fast as a gazelle, and felt empowered by the strength in my long coltish legs. The rush of wind in my hair and my legs and arms pumping in rapid rhythm was exhilarating. I was easily winning by several yards when, just like a colt, I took a misstep and tumbled down, cutting my knee on a sharp rock in the process.

Over the years, my racing scar was eventually joined by other scars: scars from other athletic events, scars from curling iron burns, poison ivy, and even scars from two c-sections. All were the results of good times or precious gifts.

I know society rewards perfection and true physical beauty is thought of as unmarred and flawless, but I disagree. I realized that day at the gym, I truly love that scar. It's a permanent symbol of my inner joy and reminds me, anytime I need reminding, that I once could run faster than the wind. What no one knows is that, in my mind, I still do.

– Geriann Fitzgerald

WILD TURKEY ON A HARD ROAD

Passing to and from
a neatly formed pavement
I see the turkey,
feathers tucked, bobbling head.
What does he seek?
Where does he wander?

I am buried in empty fields
washed with morning tides
of chicory and chamomile.
Where is my tea hidden
in this native paradise?

I share a journey with the lost turkey
now crossing the bridge,
barren, concrete.
I hit the brakes,
not knowing what to expect
from a wild turkey
on a hard road.

– Lori Becherer

IMPRESSIONS FROM A PHOTOGRAPH: CIRCA 1911

You see, don't you?
This perfect life I have.
Look at my home, so well maintained.
No chipped paint, no leaning front porch.
And look - even a perfect picket fence
Surrounding my well-structured house,
Its manicured lawn,
Lush trees and full bushes.

We sit, the three of us,
On a backless bench
That cannot be seen.
It's as if we are floating
Or suspended in space
And perhaps even in time.

Peter, my husband,
Is wearing his best black suit.
The pants have pressed creases.
His gold watch chain catches the sun's light.
His vest is buttoned.
His shirt scrubbed
And starched
And ironed.

My husband's tie is off-center though
His shoes not polished or shined.
I wonder -
What will future viewers of this photograph
Make of that?

My daughter, Veronica, is pouting.
It's my lap she wants to sit on.
She leans toward me
But I do not look at her.
I dare not touch her.

My dress also has been pressed.
But the pastel yellow material
Is now wrinkled.
I fold my hands on my lap.
What else is there to do?
I place my foot forward
As I should.
As does Peter.
But I cannot force a smile.

There will be more children.
Two daughters and a son.
We will have a life together.

I should be happy.
I should be.
But I cannot force a smile.

Someday
There will be a granddaughter,
Veronica's youngest child.
She will study this photograph
And look into my soul.
She will understand
Why I could not force a smile.

– Roselyn Mathews

BLACK AND WHITE

traveling life
      looking for black and white
            finding grey

right and wrong
      black and white
            lines are drawn

some easy to follow
some with blurred edges

black jumps out
      distorting patterns
            intended to be even

white shadows black
      causing grey
            without distinct lines

another conundrum
another reflection

black
      white
            grey

– Patricia Robert

THROUGH THE WATER'S EYE

On this solemn Sunday morning I discover a turtle shell washed up against the pond's edge. Bleached from summer's light, it glows against the rich umber mud. Segments of the decomposed house now float free in the water. The skull lies near with empty orbits staring at me. I reach into the water and place the amazing armature into my hand. This is God's handiwork.

Perched beside the pond, I hear the water's pulsing heart. I dip my fingers into the ripples. They embrace my hand with the comforting clasp of a friend. Holding my palm still against the velvet surface, the water climbs to surround me; all of me that I am willing to give.

A lanky bullfrog startles me by jumping out from a tuft of grass. In his wake he disturbs a small patch of moss that lays against the bank. The moss, mustard green, glistens with snail shells, lost wings, water bugs and a universe of amoebic life. Am I living in such a universe, where I am but a specimen, an amoeba touching nothing more than the patch of moss presented for my existence? Do I glisten?

The water speaks to me in my dreams; it soothes, tempts, commands. I heed Life's messages. A wall of water surges across the flat cornfields and I am afraid. I search for empty bottles on a stony beach. Fish gravitate from the waters to the skies. Is this my dreaming mind or my reality? I don't want to know the difference. It is only through blissful blindness that I can see in both dimensions and know that there are things I cannot control; even though sometimes I search in vain and other times take too much for granted.

The wind's whispers cease and the water lies still and black like the buckets of used oil sitting in the tractor shed. The silence speaks of a time when my worries were inconsequential, when I wallowed in the quiet nothingness that blessed me. With a blink of the water's eye, I am transported to the present where I understand that the beauty of life lies in the stillness of simplicity. It is not about the grandness of what

I do in my life; but rather, it is about allowing simple life to conceive grandness in me.

Like the turtle's broken shell, life is a puzzle. Sometimes, the pieces that fit together will not be joined until late in the journey. Sometimes the pieces won't fit together at all, no matter how hard I try. And sometimes, when I least expect it, I surprise myself with an unlikely match, that fits together perfectly.

The turtle has completed its journey, but I continue on mine. May the gentle waves never wash me aside, and may I tow only necessities on my back.

– Lori Becherer

SPECTRAL ILLUMINATION

Birth
found me helpless
yet demanding
full of mystery
with the gift of life
just enjoying simplicity
always trusting and exploring
my conscience unstained
enduring the struggle
for independence

Youth
brought the immensity of life itself
beginnings of growing regrets
and powerless disgust
pursuing, joining, crossing, separating
celebrating personal exploration
but suffering pain and loneliness
my face a reflection without fame
still learning and growing
almost ready to expel from my cocoon

Maturity
crowded with memories
and tranquil dignity
enlightened through spectral illumination
touched with compassion and sorrow
fearing conspiracy and death
yet finding joy and release
departing my empty husk
finding final surrender...and freedom

– Gea Pierce

A PHOTO OF MY MIND

heading west on Market Street to Tucker
tens of thousands of miniature white lights
decorate trees and are reflected in the
floor-to-ceiling windows of
sterile steel and concrete buildings

the early evening city scene becomes
an enchanted fairy land
a scene on a Christmas card
tears come to my eyes
and I do not know why
I am so moved

I feel surrounded by goodness and happiness
and yet - there is something pulling at me
a sense of urgency, a need
to be doing something productive
even as I am spellbound by the
magic of the scene around me

I want to cry out
Stop the car - right now!
I need to get out and become
one with this scene
to become lost in it
so that I can find
that thing
that is calling to me,
drawing me into it

Stop the car!
Stop this spinning, this whirling!
I need to slow down the merry-go-round
to rest, to be alone, to walk, to dream
to be
as I head west on Market Street to Tucker
amid tens of thousands of miniature white lights

– Roselyn Mathews

78

AT A THRESHOLD

To dance a Bulerias to Flamenco played with passion
in red ruffled skirt over black leotard.
To take down my bodhrun from the wall above my table
and find someone to teach me to make it come alive.

To replace the penny whistle that I bought in Dublin.
To forgive the one who took it from me while I looked away.
To cast in watercolors a spring green forest
with wild geese flying under skies of grey.

To plant a tranquil garden, a shady spot to rest,
and read, and practice pranayama, and to meditate.
To seek out trails of beauty and reclaim the joy I knew
in running as to music in a rhythmic, steady gait.

To suspend my own thoughts and listen more intently
to the ones who love me and the ones I love.
To break my isolation and cross a few thresholds
and open my door a little wider now and then.

To write down the stories I learned from my mother
so she will be assured of her influence.
To move toward attaining the peace that comes with knowing
That I will not die with my Dance not danced.

– Elizabeth Parker

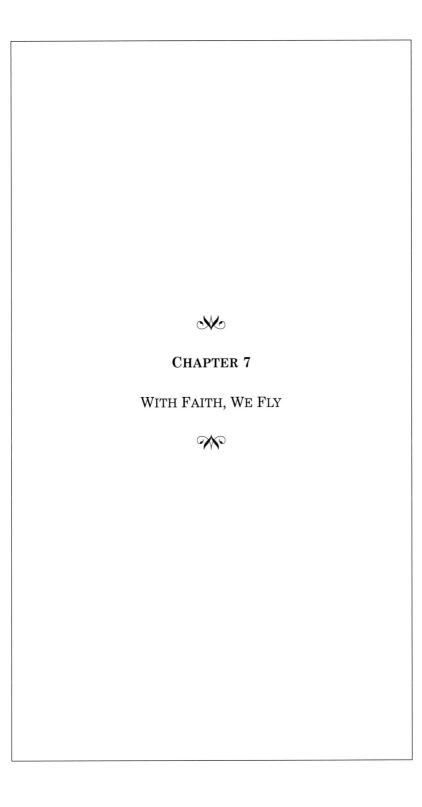

CHAPTER 7

WITH FAITH, WE FLY

WITH FAITH

With faith

> we glide upon
> the valley of the shadow
> and fear nothing
> for God provides.

> On a breath and a promise
> we cast our wings wide to
> soar higher than a mountain's peak
> and deeper than the sky's blue.

With faith

> we fly.

– Lori Becherer

THE ANSWER IS IN THE QUESTION – WHERE?

Some days are like a whirlwind, out of control -
days as stressful as being in a maze, or a struggle like
driving lost in a dense fog. I keep looking in the great
hide-and-seek game...all that searching and peeking.
Where is the deep peace and true meaning?
It's not out there. It's not from them.
It's not from that place, or staying in the race.
Time to be still and listen...a voice
quieter than the softest whisper
touches my soul
It becomes clear
I know You are here
I found the answer
in the question -
Where?
Your peace is
within me
here!

– Donna Schenk

A HEALING PSALM

As quickly as switching out a light
Without an ounce of mercy
My dreams are crushed
Is this more than I can bear?

Wanting to escape this raw reality
Yet, the shattered glass
That was my treasure
Lay all around me

So lost...where do I turn?
Desperately reaching out
As if blind, groping in the dark
Searching for direction

By God's grace I find
The Book of Psalms, "The Lord opens
The eyes of the blind, lifts burdens
Of those bent beneath their loads"

As if held in a comforting embrace
My heavenly Father assures
Faith and trust begin to restore
As doubt and fear erase

Now, each day I give my heartache to You, Lord
You give me healing in Your Sacred Presence
A renewed strength and a new courage
Trembling and foreboding no more

A wave of hope rises within me
Like the bright morning sun
Full of Your Light, Lord
I am transformed

– Donna Schenk

A SPECIAL SERVICE

Unable to attend our Sunday service
The week following my surgery
And feeling the weight of concerns
I began to think *poor me*

Struggling with the afternoon heat
I wandered in the backyard to the shade
Knowing I missed this time in church
I folded my hands and closed my eyes to pray

A gentle breeze cooled me and slowly
I began to feel our Lord's peace
Reflecting on my blessings...I gave thanks
Then sensed His presence in a special way

I found His creatures were having a service
Of their own, and it was time for song
The robins and wrens were in chorus
As the cardinals chirped the verses

Eagerly jumping in to take part
The lively tree frog screeched
Amused, I thought of a lady near my pew
Louder than most but unable to carry a tune

Just as I opened my eyes, I saw a sparrow fly
Comforted, I recalled a verse from the Good Book
"If God takes care of the smallest birds in the air..."
I should have faith that He will take care of me

I didn't have to go to the beautiful building of brick
To worship, I found fellowship right under His trees
And it was not necessary to kneel or sit in a pew
To be touched by the healing Love from above

– Donna Schenk

SEW (SOUL) WORK

Writers express it in a poetic rhyme
An artist uses strokes of color with paint and brush
My works are simple crocheted creations
Weaving with thread and needle

The thread slides through my fingers
In a relaxing rhythm, as the needle reaches up
Joining threads and letting others drop
A perfect time to reflect, and let go of stress

Counting stitches and rows
As I sew, in the stillness I recall
Warm memories of friends and family
I find I am counting many blessings, too

The work of sewing is not so much a chore
Such quiet moments...not really so alone
As much is shared with our Father
And a special time to listen to Him, too

Discovering that as I stitch, not only am I changing
Ordinary strands of thread into special gifts
But that this soul work
Is changing me, too

– Donna Schenk

DIVINE DANCE

There is a melody you can barely hear
Resonating deep inside
It is calling...

Turn the music on, beloved one
With the lyrics I have written
Your dance will be graced-full

Turn the music on, dear one
Embrace My love
Slowly follow My rhythm

Don't be afraid when you stumble
Trust that My loving arms
Will never fail

Listen...there are angelic sounds
All around
That will raise you up

Your life will become a sonata
A heavenly harmony
To those you meet

No, this Divine Dance is not for two
The concerto of My love
Is for the whole dance floor

Turn the music on, beloved one
I extend My hand
Will you accept this dance?

– Donna Schenk

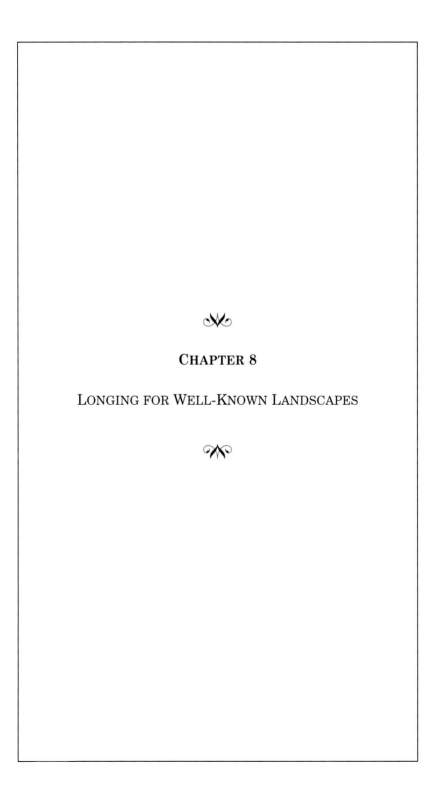

CHAPTER 8

LONGING FOR WELL-KNOWN LANDSCAPES

In Celebration of My Home

It takes only a vacation for me to fully appreciate the gifts of coming home: the familiarity, the comfort, and the sense of belonging. The initial excitement of preparing for a long-awaited vacation, viewing new scenery, exploring different areas of the country soon give way to a longing in me. It's the longing for the well-known landscapes, crops and trees of home.

I have lived in both the city and the country, and I know for certain where my heart lies. I know that endless expanses of blue sky, interrupted only by an occasional silo or church steeple brings me much peace. My eyes seek out and settle on the sky lovingly and often. It is a salve for my soul, especially when the sun shares its rising and setting with me each day. Such a simple, essential thing–yet to so many others, no more important than the blink of an eye.

Another miracle for me is watching small, stout corn plants stretch and grow, becoming tall and graceful. So much plant for one precious ear of corn. On a windy summer's day, the sight of a crop of dark green corn stalks bending and blowing in the wind is as sensual as a dancer's movements. Soon enough, though, the fluidity is gone. The summer's heat and dryness turn the dancing plants brittle, brown and still, awaiting the harvest–the gathering of the season's bounty.

I know there is much more beauty out there in the world, more varied and unusual than to what my eyes are accustomed. But were you to tell me that I would no longer see the changing of the seasons, the velvet green, then golden sprays of wheat fields, the tassel-topped milo and the wind in the willow trees that I love so well, I would mourn as though a friend had died. My Midwest home is my own: fertile, ever changing and always the same.

– Geriann Fitzgerald

SLIDING SOUTH

On a white beach
in a blue chair
the sky seemed anchored
to the ground
by high, thin clouds.
In between
pushed by the wind
gray clouds moved
to the south -
giving us the
impression
we were
sliding
that
way
too.

– Melany Nitzsche

CALHOUN AND OTHER BRIDGES

He packed the night before, hoisting from the basement
boots, overalls, gun and rabbit skin hat.
I heard my mother fill his thermos and his metal lunch box
in the flurry of his leaving before dawn on Sundays.

While my sisters and I lingered in our beds before Mass
he and his dogs crossed by ferry to Calhoun,
wild, rugged, rural, unglaciated,
cut off by great rivers, much yet undisturbed.

On trails flecked with arrowheads left by long-gone tribesmen,
with access from the farmers, he carried his shotgun.
Through forest, field and meadow, he tracked deer and rabbit.
Or, in blinds on lakes he awaited ducks and geese.

Only serious hunters did he allow to join him,
fellow Druids, unrepentent all for missing Mass.
While he hunted, my sisters and I scattered to the school yard
and the park and the woods for hours of busy play.

In the woods, we fished for crawdads in a stream,
hiked an old trail, climbed Devil's Rock.
With pounding hearts, we crept across a bridge
formed by a collapsed fence suspended between two crests,
then stopped at an abandoned railroad bridge at trail's end.

On his return at sunset, we met his station wagon,
fearful, yet curious to learn what he got.
"Got cold" or "got back," he said when empty handed.
But if we saw kill, we cried and ran away.

As I go to work at dawn, I feel the four walls of my office
and I think of Calhoun, its great blue heron, bald eagles,
bluffs, valleys, meadows, fields, lakes and rivers,
and I wonder, if it was hunting that drew him to Calhoun.

– Elizabeth Parker

NIGHTFALL

Sneaking up on daylight
    like a cat who creeps surreptitiously
        toward her prey, night approaches

Feathery wisps overshadow billowing clouds
    which layer whispers of intrigue
        on this autumn evening

As dusk encroaches on daylight
    skeletal shadow-trees play silhouettes
        against a purple expanse

Purple fades to grey
    grey enfolds charcoal
        then ebony

– Patricia Robert

DEAR NEDERLAND

Dear Nederland,

I have a confession to make. A flag colored RED, WHITE, and BLUE adorns my home. The colors are yours, but the design is not. My love for you has never lessened, my pride in you stands stronger than ever, and your national anthem still brings tears to my eyes.

Until the day I die, the roots of my being will be deeply imbedded in the Dutch clay, which my forefathers unwaveringly claimed from the ocean. I will always be a part of your people, your nation, and your race.

Life has a way of moving us, for reasons sometimes unknown. I have come to love this land where I live called *America*. The people of this country had already mixed the bouillabaisse of cultures before I ever arrived, and I know why they stayed. This country bid me welcome and brought me love and prosperity. It showed me its beauty in so many forms.

I know I belong in America now, but I will always be your child.

Forever,
Your Gea

– Gea Pierce

DELTA SYNERGY

From the Earth's farthest corners
Come the stories, come the dances,
Come the stitches, paints and brushes,
Come the instruments and songs.
They all flow into the river
And the river works its gris-gris
Infusing mighty essence
Of the planet's richest soil.

Now sail on down the river.
See the swirling, bubbling whirlpools?
Every pool's a stewing cauldron
With its own alchemy.
Each is ancient and yet brand new,
Familiar, yet exotic,
Defiant, bold, brazen,
America born.

– Elizabeth Parker

NIGHTWATCH

Quiet steps along the hall
Huge clock on the other wall
Slowly marking off the hours
The comfort of a cross above it

The visitor bell rings, quiet falls
A bedtime prayer in the corridor echoes
A door light gleams as someone calls
For help from nurses on the floor

My door is opened, a ray of light
By me a quiet presence stands
To take my vital signs
Take more blood, hold my hand

I surrender to my helplessness
In my weakness I bless this place
I know here is healing, care and grace
My only hope for recovery

– Elizabeth Hoffman

CUSHENDALL

Can I come up to Antrim, James, to your glen in Cushendall
Enfolded by the mountains muting down the midnight sun?
Can I watch your border collies herd the sheep behind your cottage
and hike the glens, washed with waterfalls and drenched with mist?

Is the forest still as lush, James, the green as deep and varied?
Does the sun still trickle through and make diamonds of the dew?
Is the air still rich with power to fuel the mind to wander?
Does the veil in the thin place[1] part as easily as before?

Let me leave behind the troubles brought about by my ambition.
Let me sit with you and learn to be cheerful again.
We can talk again of Belfast and the Troubles. They're so distant
From the fireside in your cottage in your glen at Cushendall.

Let me sit by my window opening up to the mountains
With the distant waterfalls and the sheep up high like stars.
My pen moves with such power there fueled by the glen air
Until I sleep the sleep I've never slept but in Cushendall.

– Elizabeth Parker

6th Place Saturday Writers Chapter
Missouri Writers Guild
2004 One-Page Poetry Contest

[1] *In Celtic spirituality, certain locations were called "thin places", where the division between heaven and earth was said to be at its narrowest.*

FINDING SHELTER IN LAKEVIEW PARK

Rain is quietly penciling down as I sit on a bench in Lakeview Park. The grass is a mossy green, thick and inviting. Hills slowly lower into lakes. Mature trees keep watch all around the park. It is a quiet, grey morning with a slight humidity seeping in. Picnic shelters, like the one I'm in, act as umbrellas for those who don't care to slowly soak themselves.

Not all are deterred on a Sunday morning, though. A man and a young boy have slid out into the glassy water from the banks of the lake in their johnboat. With the man standing and the boy leaning over as he sits, they conjure up the image of a miniature sail boat heading out into a miniature ocean.

A hummingbird buzzes all the way across the openness of the park–lured by the false promise of a red shirt. He doesn't seem to mind that I'm not a flower, but simply heads back from where he came. An indiscreet opening along the back wood line of the park is marked as a nature trail. A turquoise truck slowly snakes its way around the one lane road to the park exit.

Young saplings have been recently planted near the picnic shelter at the back of the park. Rain accumulates all along the roof line of the shelter until each drop hangs heavy enough to drip. Mourning doves coo loudly. Crickets, filling in the gaps on this suspended morning, change to a mellower key.

A middle-aged woman is jogging the trail along the perimeter of the park. Her running shoes steadily crunch on the gravel scattered along the asphalt path. She carries a water bottle in one hand, although simply turning her face to the pale sky should suffice on a morning like this. A brown dog follows closely behind her, matching her every step as if on a leash.

I, too, meant to walk the trails this morning, but this picnic shelter provides such a cozy picture window that I succumb to the sanctuary it provides. Walking trails will take you places, but sometimes sitting still will take you even further.

– Melany Nitzsche

CHAPTER 9

EATING LIVER SAUSAGE ON RYE
IN THE MIDDLE OF THE MISSISSIPPI

A Boat Ride Down the River

The day turned out to be crystal clear, warm and sunny, certainly beckoning. It was what my sons would call "bluebird perfect." So I played hooky. The beds stayed unmade, the dishes unwashed, the cooking and cleaning put on hold. With priorities put in their right order, it was time to go on the river.

My boys have always loved the water, be it a creek, a pond, a lake, a river, or an ocean. They are accomplished sailors, extraordinary fishermen, adventurous scuba divers, and incredible swimmers. When they invite me to go on a boat ride with them, all domestic life as I know it is put on hold.

That bluebird day I hurriedly packed a lunch. Soon after I was climbing into a 16-foot boat outfitted with a motor, depth finder, life jackets, and a steering wheel. I settled unsteadily on a middle seat and immediately turned into a female Tom Sawyer. Anticipation was churning within me. I was going on my first small boat ride down the Mighty Mississippi.

As we launched on a narrow creek that would eventually run into the big river, I watched my two grown sons pull the boat off the trailer, their strong young muscles rippling their arms. They paid no attention to the squish of wet mud as it sucked on their sandals. It was proof they had been down this wet road before.

When we shoved off, every fiber in my body was attuned to the feathery greenness around me. I could smell the woodsy water, a scent so vibrant and fresh that it promised to evaporate any worldly cares. Wispy willow branches swayed along the shore, playfully dipping into the green water to cool off their leaves.

Away from human sounds, there was a primordial quietness. Only the chirping of birds was heard as they flitted from one side of the creek to the other. This must be what paradise is like, I thought. Was I experiencing the exact same feeling as the very first human to venture here? A kindred feeling washed through me. I felt a strong warm link to that original pioneer.

We startled a large blue heron searching for a tasty fish or frog along the creek's narrow shore. It was one of several we saw on the trip. Is there anything more graceful than a heron taking off and flying, its pointed bill and slender neck leading the way, its long slim legs trailing effortlessly behind? It was headed for one of the many rookeries that dot the river's shores.

The creek was running faster now. As we reached the river, my heart skipped a beat as the boat adjusted to the swiftly flowing Mississippi, one of the greatest rivers in the world. The water was high, almost at flood stage after a week of rainfall. I thought of all the rich human history that must have taken place on this incredible body of water.

My eyes scanned the waves as I wondered about all the relics that must lie buried on the river bottom. There must be traces of Indian life. There must be clues to the exploits of explorers, soldiers, trappers, and pioneers.

Would someone one day find the bones of Hernando de Soto, the Spanish explorer who died of yellow fever and was buried in the river? How many riverboat captains, crews, and passengers had passed this way? If water could talk, what stories that muddy river could tell!

We moved along smoothly, dodging logs and debris swept down from northern floodwaters. I couldn't believe I was actually on this powerful, great river road, one that drained off a third of all America, from the Appalachians to the Rocky Mountains. Thoughts of past history were nudged aside as evidence of modern civilization came into view. Dotting the shores were energy plants, quarries, and cement plants. In the distance we saw barges hauling grain.

For a while we shut off the boat's engines and drifted, letting the current take us where it pleased. We took out the lunch I had packed and enjoyed sandwiches and a cold drink. Suddenly I realized I was eating liver sausage on rye in the middle of the Mississippi River!

I didn't want our bluebird day to end. I had joined all the others whose souls had been caught up in the mystical magic of this mighty waterway. As I scanned the shores, I half expected to see Tom Sawyer come drifting out of the river's mist on his raft, a fishing pole in his hand. Why did I feel like waving to him? The river's magic had done its work.

– *Lucy Engbring*

READING A MEDICAL ENCYCLOPEDIA

Lying in bed with a hefty volume
of medical woes, I read before I turn out the light.

Garish pictures demonstrate vivid descriptions
of symptoms that start to sound familiar.

In a fitful sleep I will dream of disease,
wondering how I survived this long

and if I'll ever wake up again.

– Melany Nitzsche

AUGUST FANTASY

As a child, I had a powerfully vivid imagination. This "gift" was further enhanced by frequent visits to an enchanted wooded area on the farm where my family lived.

The northern tract of our farm consisted of a dense woods that sloped gently to a lush fertile valley. Near the center of the valley was a clearing, carpeted with grass and wild flowers, and edged on three sides by a curving, spring-fed creek. Pure, sparkling spring water trickled continuously from jagged cracks in a limestone outcropping that fringed a deeply-shaded portion of the creek.

Even during hot, humid Midwestern summers, the atmosphere in this secluded, canopied clearing was pleasant and cool. Soft breezes danced with oak and sycamore leaves and produced a rhythmical, whispering sound. Birds chirped melodiously; squirrels scurried from branch to branch; rabbits played hide-and-seek behind tree trunks; insects chattered among themselves. And one even could sense a vast world of activity *beneath* this magical playground.

Late one August afternoon when I was nine and my sister eleven, we decided to go wading in the creek. We walked leisurely down the worn path that led to the valley, and had just crossed over the decaying tree trunk that bridged the creek banks, when we became aware of an unusual, eerie stillness. I glanced at my sister and frowned quizzically. We slowed our pace and hunched down a bit. Then, gazing straight ahead with widened eyes, we came to a dead halt.

A full miniature rainbow arched over the limestone outcropping. Steamy mist surrounded the fountain of spring water that flowed from the moss-lined crevices. Flittering around the rainbow were a half dozen or more tiny winged beings–beautiful female forms with long flowing hair, delicate facial features, and slender bodies. Their tiny feet were bare, but they were clothed in loose fitting, gauze-like gowns of various pastel hues.

My sister and I looked at each other, and at the same time silently mouthed a single word: *fairies!* We quickly returned our gaze to the tiny beings and watched their animated antics for over an hour. Then, in an instant, they were gone. With a second blink of our eyes, the rainbow and steamy mist also dissipated. In a matter of minutes, the usual woodland sounds and activities returned.

We moved silently to the edge of the creek near the limestone outcropping. As we slipped off our shoes and dipped our toes into the cool spring water, a fine, glittering dust sprinkled onto our shoulders. We glanced up to see a cluster of large, exotic butterflies fluttering playfully above us. They circled our heads twice and then vanished into the dense woods.

My sister and I never spoke again about what we witnessed that August afternoon. But we *know* what we saw. And to this day, we still believe in possibilities of all kinds...and magical, enchanted places... and soft, glittering fairy dust.

– Roselyn Mathews

THE PORTRAIT

With shadow and light a portrait forms
shades of life and death defined
wistful line and blended curve
into man's image shall entwine.

Glaring back from catching eyes
a soul reaches out to me
seeking heartfelt secrets, mystic smiles
and breath to set her free.

– Lori Becherer

OH, RIVER OF SLEEP

Standing on your steep bank
   gazing at your serene waters from afar
soothing currents allure to waves of dreams

As a lover tempts with tender kisses
   you lead me on, tease me with promises
to relax my mind and body, no stress, just rest

But not tonight, when I come near
   you reject me…my eyes pop open
deserted on this Island of the Weary again

Craving to lazily drift away, cradle me
   until my cries for dreams end, and dance
in a land that is both illusive and enlightening

So close…floating on this restful river
   blissful peace begins to swallow me, slowly
sinking into the dark abyss, where no one thinks

Oh, River of Sleep, just as I feel the touch
   of your sweet kiss–abruptly you spit me out
my eyes pop open…back on the bank **awake** again!

– Donna Schenk

THE COAT AND TALE OF MR. PENNINGTON

Warm rays of bright sunlight poured through Tom's bedroom window, waking him early Saturday morning. He lay there briefly while his clear blue eyes focused, then he rolled his lean six-foot, three-inch frame out of bed. This was the first weekend in months that he did not have to go to the office. He and his team had been working incessantly on an ad campaign for an elite, high stakes client account. Now that the project was complete, he had some down time and, starting today, he planned to make the most of it. This morning he would go for an early run, then do some photography, a hobby he enjoyed but seldom had time for.

Tom quickly changed into a pair of running shorts and a white tee shirt, smoothed his sandy-blond hair, and left his upscale New England apartment, eager to begin his day.

Five minutes later, Tom whipped his black and silver Lexus into a parking space, shoved the keys and cell phone into his pack, and headed for the trail. As he made his way along the dewy flower-fringed pathways, he noticed that the park was empty except for the occasional jogger, roller-blader or dog-walker that startled the pigeons strutting across the walk, jabbering among each other like retirees on bingo night. It was a perfect day. The pond shimmered like diamonds, reflecting the streaming rays of the early sun. Willow branches swayed sleepily back and forth in rhythm with the ebb and tide of the lazy cool breezes. Across the street, an historic country church sat on top of a small grassy knoll, its tall steeple silhouetted against the pastel hues of the morning sky. Having been partially burned in a fire many years ago, it was no longer used. However, both the church and the old cemetery next to it dating back to the early 1800's, stood as landmarks in town.

After a half-hour run, Tom began to slow his pace. Though he tried to keep up a regular exercise routine, the demanding hours at work often interfered. Never more evident than now, his oxygen deprived lungs yearning for fresh air, he paused at a park bench to take a drink of bottled water. After resting a few minutes, he took one last swallow, stood up, and grabbed the camera from his pack. He wanted to photograph some of the park's wildlife before they retreated to their hiding places, seeking refuge from curious children and their parents on picnics later that afternoon.

Just then he glimpsed a slight movement in the trees nearby, close to the road that separated the park from the old church. He saw a man, probably in his twenties, about six feet tall, wearing a long, tattered black tuxedo. A dingy, once white pleated shirt and dark cumberbun accompanied his crumpled coat. Scuffed, leather dress shoes completed his coat and tails ensemble. In one hand was a bottle of Scotch that appeared to be only a third full. He moved slowly, meandering aimlessly as he struggled to hold his body steady. Tom discreetly snapped a picture. A photograph like this would be interesting, capturing the embodiment of human sadness and despair.

Tom stepped back as the stranger approached and took a seat on the park bench. He could smell the fumes of alcohol dripping off of his breath, but that was not all. This person smelled of something old, musty and moldy. A chill seemed to emanate from his body.

"Had a rough night?" Tom asked. The man did not answer.

"My name's Tom."

Tom watched while the stranger sat quietly, looking blankly ahead.

"What's your name?"

The man remained silent.

Tom's curiosity was growing.

"Hello?" Tom leaned slightly forward. He immediately leaned back again, the smell of whiskey filling his nose and nauseating him.

The man continued to ignore him. Staring straight ahead, he lifted the bottle of Scotch to his mouth. Tom listened as the liquor washed away in waves.

"Well, guess I'd better be going," Tom turned to walk away.

"John," the stranger answered suddenly. "You asked my name. It's John Pennington."

The man looked directly at Tom now, his eyes so bloodshot that his pupils were barely visible. "Annie is meeting me there," he continued, nodding his head slowly toward the old church. "We're gonna get married."

"You're getting married there?" Tom asked. "That church isn't used anymore."

"There." The man repeated. "At two o'clock, October 2nd, 18..."

"I doubt it, but whatever you say," Tom interrupted, starting to walk away.

He took a few steps before glancing back, only to find the park bench empty. Tom's eyes scanned the park looking for the man among the trees.

Where'd he go? Tom wondered. *He was there just a second ago.* He felt uneasy as he headed for the car.

Back at home, Tom's curiosity and confusion about the man in the park continued to bother him. Hoping to find an answer, he went into the darkroom to develop the pictures he had taken that morning. Tom smiled when he saw a close up of a squirrel, completely ignorant of his paparazzi, sitting on his haunches blissfully savoring a tasty walnut. Another photo showed mallard ducks skidding onto the surface of a glistening lake as they came in for a landing. It was the absence of the drunken stranger in the next photo, however, that puzzled him. The grove of trees stood alone. Tom's heart rate increased slightly as he quickly placed the picture back into the developer. *Maybe I didn't leave it in long enough*, he thought to himself. A few minutes later, he pulled the dripping photo back out and held it up to examine. Still, all he could see were trees. Baffled, Tom tossed the print aside and quickly left the darkroom.

Tom had plans that night to have dinner with his girlfriend, Stacy, and some of their friends. Throughout the evening they laughed and talked, but Tom's mind was on the events from earlier that morning. He kept remembering the man stating the date as eighteen something. The experience continued to mystify him.

"Are you okay?" Stacy asked Tom at one point during dinner. "You seem a little quiet."

Tom shrugged. "Just tired from work I guess." But he knew that was not the truth. The deep, nagging feeling persisted.

A little while later, Stacy again asked Tom why he was being so quiet. He hesitated, then told the group what had happened earlier that day.

"Oh, come on, forget about it," his friends chided. "What do you care? He was just a drunk."

"But you should have seen him," Tom tried to explain. "I can't put my finger on it, but there was something different...really odd about him!"

Later, their friends decided to go on for more drinks. Tom did not feel like going so he and Stacy went their own way.

"Let's stop by that old church on the way home," Tom began.

"Why?" Stacy inquired.

"I want to see it," Tom went on.

"But it's already dark. What do you think you'll see?"

"I don't know. Just come with me, okay?"

"Fine," Stacy agreed, a bit exasperated.

Grabbing a flashlight from the glove compartment, he and Stacy got out of the car in front of the church. They walked up the steps to the front door, finding it padlocked. Then they walked around the outside of the building.

"Tom, this is creepy." Stacy shuddered, her mind flashing back to stories of the sinister and menacing, spun so many times around summer campfires with friends during her childhood. "What are you looking for?"

"I told you, I don't know," Tom answered. "I just need to check this out."

"Then you go," Stacy replied abruptly, turning to leave. "This isn't exactly what I had in mind when you said we'd go out tonight. I'll be in the car."

Tom took a deep breath and scanned the premises for a few more minutes, but saw nothing unusual. He didn't really know why he was there either but, nonetheless, he was. He was just about to leave, when something compelled him to walk toward the black wrought iron fence guarding the old cemetery. He pushed open the corroded gate, and with his flashlight, scanned the marble stones. He walked gingerly between the monuments, trying to read some of the names and dates on them, although some of the etchings had worn away over the years. There were beloved mothers, fathers, brothers, sisters, daughters and sons. According to the inscriptions, typhoid had taken many of them.

A cool night wind began to blow from the northwest. Tom pulled his jacket in closer.

"Let's go Tom, it's getting cold!" Stacy called impatiently from the car window.

"I'll be there in a minute!" he answered firmly. As he turned to leave, the beam from his flashlight shone on another headstone. Tom read the name engraved on the marble as icy chills shot up his spine.

"JOHN PENNINGTON, 1855-1878. Beloved son, brother and fiancé...died of a broken heart."

"He was twenty-three years old," Tom murmured, his heart pounding.

The whispering wind through the barren branches began to take on a vaguely familiar sound. John Pennington's voice drifted through the night. "I will not leave you, Annie. I love you. I love you," the voice sobbed softly.

Tom swung his flashlight toward the sound. The beam cut like a beacon across the headstones until it faded into the darkness. He saw no one as the eerie voice continued briefly, then melted back into the wind. As he searched, his eyes caught a glint of light reflecting from a nearby grave. Dried leaves crunched beneath his feet as he stepped closer to get a better look. His pulse raced as he stared at the empty bottle of Scotch lying in the weeds. Tom fell to his knees and brushed away the debris from the base of the marble stone. He shuddered, the bony hands of fear gripping him as he read the inscription:

"ANNIE SMITHTON, 1852-1877. Typhoid took our beloved daughter, sister and fiancée."

He dropped his flashlight at the foot of Annie's grave and ran toward the car. He threw the car in gear and sped off.

"What happened back there?" Stacy prodded him.

Tom didn't answer. His eyes were fixed on the road ahead.

"Tom?" Stacy tried again to get his attention.

Still, he would not answer. Only once did he glance in the rearview mirror at the old church, then he quickly looked away. Tom did not know exactly what had happened back at the cemetery. He could only guess, and he was certain no one would believe him. Perhaps it was better that no one ever know. Perhaps some things are just better left alone.

– Meg Bergmann

Dr. Jazz Says

On a hot, steamy day
Dr. Jazz says, "Improvise."
Lighten up, bare your feet
Shrug off your responsibilities
For an hour or two–at least
And c o o o o o l down.

With cubes clinking in a tall, cold glass
Head for the shade tree, lie down, stretch
Feel the green blades caress your neck,
Tickle your toes, mess with your head.

"The simple secret is," Dr. Jazz says,
"Take what's available. Mold it, style it,
Fit it to your life."

Easier said than done, you say?
"Not so," Dr. Jazz says,
"Once you learn to improvise."

– Roselyn Mathews

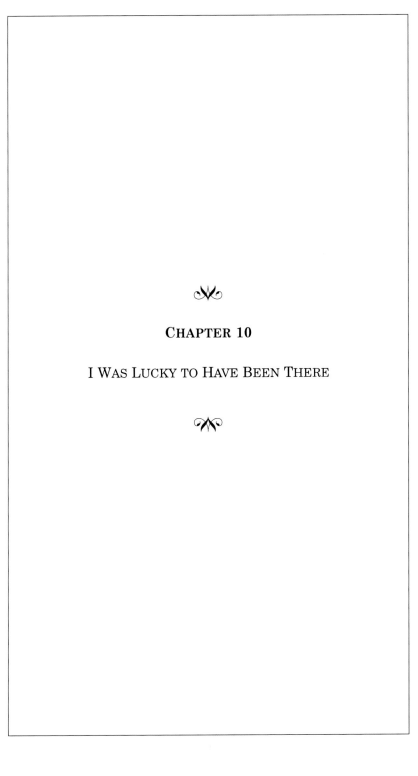

CHAPTER 10

I WAS LUCKY TO HAVE BEEN THERE

Through His Eyes

Some say it is the small things in life that really matter, not the big ones like new cars, huge homes or expensive vacations. Consider, for example, the gentle tapping of a spring rain as it rinses and replenishes the earth, the fragrance of freshly cut grass, the pageantry of fireflies, or the serenade of crickets on a steamy summer night. Imagine the thrill as you escape the blazing afternoon sun and slip into a crystal blue lake, the cool water washing over you. All you have to do is shut your eyes and you can taste the sweet satisfaction of a cold, creamy banana split on a lazy August evening.

Pleasures they are; still, so many of these day-to-day occurrences are taken for granted until something or someone reminds you of them by waving them in your face, repeatedly, loud and clear, until you stop and take notice.

"Mommy, I got a surprise for you," he said as he ran into the family room, his shorts piled around his ankles. "Come here to the bathroom!" he ordered me. "C'mon!"

All I could see was the back of his head, arms and rosy rear end cheeks as he turned, his little legs carrying him as fast as they could down the hall toward the bathroom.

"C'mon Mom," he hollered again as he scurried, somewhat agitated that I wasn't immediately racing behind him.

"I'm coming," I sighed as I begrudgingly hoisted myself up from the couch that I had just collapsed on for the very first time that night. Mind you, it was 8:30 p.m. As I stood up, I glanced at a pile of crumpled laundry smugly staring at me from across the room. I gave it a dirty look as I passed it on the way to follow the voice of my very eager child.

"Mom?" he called impatiently.

"I'm here," I replied as I approached the bathroom door.

"I got a surprise for you!"

"What is it?" I asked, as though I had no idea what my surprise could possibly be.

"Look! I went potty in the big potty-chair, just like you and Daddy! I'm bigger now, 'cause I ate all my food today!"

He was overflowing with childlike innocence. His exuberance was contagious.

"Yeah, alright!" I cheered. "Way to go Jimmy! Give me a high-five!" His little hand smacked full force into mine. I felt a wave of enthusiasm wash over me. My heart felt warm and full and so very much alive. I never felt this way when *I* went to the bathroom.

Jimmy's big hazel-colored eyes sparkled. "I even made bubbles!" he pointed out, as he and I peered into the bowl together.

"Yes, you did! You're such a big boy. I love you!" I reached down, kissed him on top of his head, then got down on my knees and gave him a huge hug.

"You're squ-e-e-e-zing me," he gasped, still grinning.

"Oh, sorry," I composed myself as I stood up. "I'm so proud of you, Jimmy!" I said a little more softly now. "Okay, pull your pants up, flush and wash your hands," I instructed him. He did just that and off he went, racing back to play with his cars and trucks.

As I stood at the sink, drying puddles of water left on the counter and wiping splashes from the mirror, I noticed the bathroom, only a minute ago full of cheers and laughter, now echoed with silence. The realization that my son was growing up so very fast suddenly hit me. I knew my diaper changing days would soon be over. I hung up the towel, glanced at the toilet, and turned out the light. I walked into the family room where Jimmy sat, contentedly playing with his toys. All I wanted to do was hold him as bittersweet emotions of sadness, happiness and pride began to compete within me.

For the next two days it seemed like Jimmy had to use the bathroom every 15 minutes and, every 15 minutes, I was summoned by my son to perform my cheerleading duties. Each time, he'd burst with pride at his achievement, sharing his joy so freely. I was lucky to have been there to share this and so many other special moments with him, and through his eyes, be reminded of the splendor of the simple things in life.

Those memories are now indelibly etched deep within my heart. I know as an adult, years from now, Jimmy won't remember the magic we shared that day, but I always will...and I will smile.

– Meg Bergmann-Jimmy's mom,

September 15, 2004

Seven Haiku in Celebration of Ordinary Things

The tang of wood smoke
Robust russets, golds and plums
Sure signs of autumn

Brown caterpillars
Hustle across the pavement
Autumn migration

Shapeless shadows dance
In dark silent harmony
Haunted twilight scene

Spiring church steeple
Framed by cloudless autumn sky
View of perfect prayer

Sounds muffled by fog
Ghostly outline of ferry
Early morning pier

Waterfront landscape
Sidewalk café on Cape Cod
People-watching treat

The old barn door leans
Outward on rusted hinges
Imperfect beauty

– Roselyn Mathews

SOMETIMES, I THOUGHT...

No matter how she felt
Or how hot the humid summer day got
My mama cooked, cleaned and canned
The next day, she would get up
And cook, clean and can, again
Sometimes, I thought
Mama wouldn't have enough time for me

My older brothers got all the really hard chores
It seemed like my little sister got the easy ones
But when I'd get the never-ending
Hot job of picking green beans,
I'd never want her to know, but
Sometimes, I thought
Mama was a little mean

She had to be
As strong as any man,
Carrying those huge wet loads of wash
Up the narrow cellar stairs to the line
Following behind with mine
Sometimes, I thought
Mama made it very hard to complain

I was never sure whether the work was done
Or if she gave in to exhaustion
But I'd find Mama lying on the couch, on her side
Even though she'd usually be asleep, I'd sneak
Into the space, behind the bend in her knees
Sometimes, I thought
Oh, what a special place–just Mama and me

– Donna Schenk

FRAGMENTS

Deep red geranium blossoms bursting forth
From a chipped cobalt-blue and white enamel pot
A wide, crooked windowsill painted thick creamy white
Images set against a background swatch of sparkling blue sea
Vivid fragments of a hazy scene floating through her memory

Lacy white curtain, faded rain stain on its lower edge,
Fluttering in the morning breeze from the open window
Warm, salty air licking her bare, sun-burned shoulders
A single creak from a foot step on the uneven plank floor
Vivid fragments of a hazy scene floating through her memory

Noisy seagulls, their white wings working,
Swoop and float and squawk incessantly
The woman stirs from a dream of her lover
In his white sailor uniform, holding a red warning flag
Vivid fragments of a hazy scene floating through her memory

The dreamer awakens, her sea-blue eyes bright with anticipation
Her long hair, white and thinning now; her body small
She sees him smiling, racing home to her in the shiny red convertible
His eyes fixed on the road ahead, daring to believe in his invincibility
Vivid fragments of a hazy scene floating through her memory

– Roselyn Mathews

COMFORT ME

No warm hand in mine
Just fond old memories
Like this faded afghan
Lying warm on my knees
       Comfort me

The room no longer hums
With their cheerful chatter
Just the repeating squeaks
Of this old wooden rocker
       Comfort me

No soft smile to greet me
Each morning, as long ago
Only silent faces on these
Treasured family photos
       Comfort me

Making a meal such a chore
No helpful hands anymore
Days pass without seeing
A face, just occasional calls
       Comfort me

Now, no longer alone, finally
Agree to go to a new Home
Thankfully, these caring folks
Are my new family that daily
       Comfort me

– Donna Schenk

THE SUMMERS OF HER CHILDHOOD

Her childhood memories remain painted
in the colors of evening rainbows,
fields of purple-flowering clover
and golden wheat waving in the summer breeze.

She would fall asleep on those long ago
   summer nights
In seersucker baby doll pajamas
While a symphony of crickets, punctuated by
   the throaty thrill of the night frogs,
Serenaded her even as she slept.

She lay on crisp white cotton sheets
That had hung on the clothes line
   earlier that day,
Flapping in the wind like the sails of a
Schooner she had read about once.

And even now when she closes her eyes
   and remembers,
She can still smell the sweet fragrance
   of honey suckle
Mingled with the scent of roses
That wafted through her open bedroom window
Wrapping her in a cocoon of innocence
That lingered through the night
Through all the summers of her childhood.

– Roselyn Mathews

1st Place Southwestern Illinois College
2002 Poetry Contest

Honorable Mention The Wednesday Club
of St. Louis 2002 Poetry Contest

(Simultaneous Submissions)

HAIKU MEMORIES

Remember

> Remember sensing
> warm chocolate chip cookies
> through unopened doors?

Remember

> Remember our mirth
> at the movies when no one
> else saw the humor?

Remember

> Remember the night
> our reach exceeded our grasp?
> Exhilaration.

– Patricia Robert

THE LAST GIFT

John made a quick U-turn after he passed the ruins of the cemetery. The urge to see the old house was too strong. They had been newlyweds and rented the old farmhouse after they fell in love with the house and its beautiful surroundings.

Carefully, he pulled into the dilapidated driveway, shocked by the forlorn mutilation of the house and the "condemned" sign in the front yard. He stood next to his car, absorbed in the silence and the view.

The windows were like blind eyes, blinking in the sun. The sagging gutters resembled eyebrows under the bad hair day that once was the roof. The carport was only standing on two legs, the third one broken at the knee. Years of sunburns without protection from the elements explained blistering paint on the exposed body. The house moaned and rattled in its slow death; the sound matched a family of bullfrogs that was practicing their chorus lines.

Ignoring the warning sign, John wandered closer to the house, surrounded by the familiar scents of wild onions and fish. He inspected the broken leg of the carport and entered the breezeway, where the frayed string still hung from an empty light socket.

Every spring the barn swallows attempted to build their nest on this socket, only to have it destroyed by the big black snake that lived in the hollow tree by the window.

Sometimes the snake ate the eggs; sometimes he devoured the babies when they gave away their location by loud demands for food. The frantic parents usually rebuilt a week later, but they never successfully raised a family.

The door was unlocked and he entered the kitchen, which still emitted a faint scent of nutmeg and garlic from the broken pantry. The tile floor he had installed was still there, reminding him of their little guy riding his brand new tricycle. That was twelve years ago. The little guy was now a tall teenager, involved in football and golf.

John opened the small door under the sink. The same floor under the pipes was still there; he must have done a good job. The sight took him back to the night they played cards with his in-laws. The mouse-trap under the sink had snapped shut and they decided to take care of the trap later, but a loud noise under the sink had rushed them into the kitchen. They had found a large black snake, which was attempting to eat the mouse with the trap, until the screams of the women made the reptile choose a fast exit. The next day he had fixed the cabinet, replacing the rotten floor with a solid piece of wood.

John walked into the living room and admired the view. He remembered his wife silhouetted in front of this window, her body swollen with their child. Her pregnancy had softened her and the birth of their son had enriched their love even more.

This old house had given them so much. Life had been so much simpler then. They were so poor and felt so rich.

He tried to open the patio door and found it was unlocked. He stepped onto the small sagging deck and remembered the horror on his son's face after he had introduced the small toad to his pet turtle, while playing in the pool. The boy's desperate cries, so long ago, seemed to linger in the afternoon breeze.

The big tree still proudly reached out over the patio, providing the living room with afternoon shade. The trunk that used to house the large black snake had been hollow for many years.

Once, during a picnic, a friend thought the snake had been placed as a prank, until it moved and the girl resembled a frantic mother bird with flapping arms and loud screeches. The memory brought a smile to his face and he decided to go back inside and visit the bedroom. John entered their love nest with the familiar anticipation; their bodies had been *wonderlands*, the rest of the world a minor detail.

A movement in the closet startled him. He anticipated a reunion with the snake, but it was a tiny kitten, barely old enough to walk. He looked around for its nest and the mother cat while going from room to room. But the little creature was all alone, following him and trying to get his attention with a very small voice. It settled in his warm hands like it belonged there, and created a soft rumbling sound deep inside its tiny body.

John wondered about the chances of survival for this small creature and a surge of protectiveness made him hold the kitten closer to his body where it fell asleep. The little animal looked exhausted and malnourished, its tiny ribs visible through the fur. He would take the kitten to the local vet, have it examined, and take it home with him.

Slowly, he walked back to his car with the kitten. He did not look back at the old house. John was too preoccupied with its last gift.

– Gea Pierce

This poem is for my sister who accompanied me through the adventure of childhood.

LAZY AUGUST NIGHTS

When the August moon dances behind gently swaying maple branches
And elusive shadows change partners in the silver light
I remember two young sisters running and laughing

They carried Mason quart jars
With holes punched in the lids
And chased after fire flies
The warm summer air steamed
With rich farm smells
      musky, cut alfalfa ready for baling
      pungent manure drying in the barn yard
      spicy tomatoes left for ripening
         on the back porch steps

Later, after baths scented with Avon Bubble Bath
The two sisters lay in bed whispering and giggling
Heads at the foot of the bed
To better catch traces of night breezes
Drifting in through opened windows
From the kitchen the mother called to them
To stop talking and get to sleep
Moist, warm hands hurried to mouths to stifle one last giggle
Slender, child bodies stretched
Mouths emitted yawns
Sleepy eyes closed

Soon, the only sounds in the still night were the chirping of crickets
And the occasional distant barking of dogs
Accompanying the girls' gentle breathing

Before long, mother and father also would go to bed
And the lights in the white frame farm house
Clicked off

Outside, the luminous full moon opened its arms
As it bathed the house in its maternal softness
And slowly pulled the oceans' tides across time

– Roselyn Mathews

1st Place Southwestern Illinois College
2004 Poetry Contest

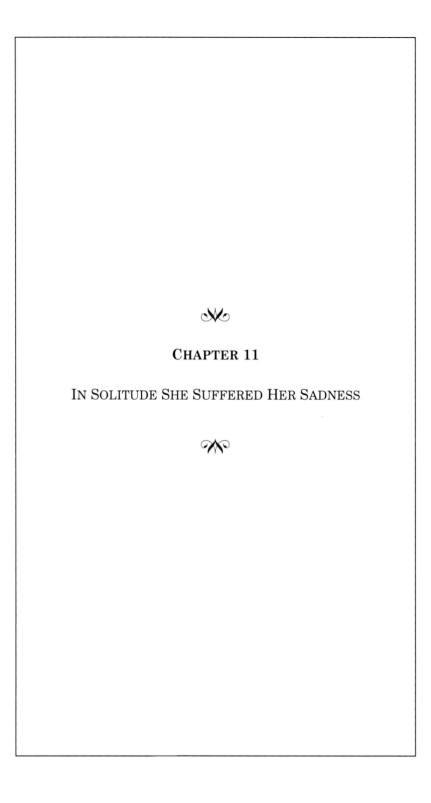

CHAPTER 11

IN SOLITUDE SHE SUFFERED HER SADNESS

Paschal Requiem

She dressed her daughters in seasonal colors,
lavender, robin's-egg blue, baby pink,
topped with matching capes she had made.
What "goooorgeous fabric," she purred feather-soft.

Her suit, as always, demure understatement,
amplified her searing beauty.
Father Shaw caught his breath on sight of her
even though he could not see her dark eyes
downcast as they were, awaiting Communion.

She engaged her daughters in the season:
the greening, the flowering, the birth and rebirth,
renewal, resurrection, He is Risen, Alleluia.
Teaching her girls the songs of the birds,
Shooing the blue jay from the wren house,
Preening the garden's lilacs and lilies,
Gushing over baby asparagus,
Cooing at winter-born babies in strollers.
Why did she fail to get caught in the updraft?

In autumn at least she had company.
The death of the flora and flight of the wildlife,
the dread of winter and bitter and grey
and brown and dark brought many her way
to sorrow and sadness and ache of despair.

But in the spring, while others rejoiced,
in solitude she suffered her sadness.
The loneliness fueled her covert spiral,
and she disengaged from life's frail hold
in the greening, flowering flush of spring.

– Elizabeth Parker

MY MOTHER KNEW

My mother did not tell me
they were coming

but she knew

they marched into our country
like a river of aggression

I did not know about such things

sounds of marching feet
causing unfamiliar vibrations

the air was still and so was I

louder and louder
closer all the time

wanting

to run and hide
yet wanting to see

feelings of fear and doom

my pounding heart in rhythm
with their marching boots

my mother's hands

gripping my shoulders
her tears falling on my head

I circled my arms

backwards around her legs
to comfort her

she needed me like I needed her

– Gea Pierce

THIS IS HOW I SEE YOU STILL

for Matt

As a belted kingfisher perched on the edge of a rural pond
Alert and agile deer along the hemline of the woods
Wintering bald eagles in flight where rivers converge
Wild turkeys scratching among a newly harvested field

Large iguanas sunning themselves on jutting Caribbean rocks
Red-tailed hawks biding their time from the tops of their humble throne
The March return of purple martins with their acrobatic swirls
The anticipated new growth on a cluster of white pines

The reflection of our relationship in Bob Kolbrener's *Stratus Clouds*
Red-bellied woodpeckers splitting seeds in cracks of cedar beams
The collective howl of coyotes seeping in through an evening's open window
Cedar waxwings in a crabapple, flowers already fallen

All these things existed before, but now my focus has sharpened
One more gift you've given me, another layer in my life
I look for them still, seeking the solace of finding you in their form
This is how I see you still and know you haven't gone

– Melany Nitzsche

REMEMBER AND HONOR

In Memory of Michael Huelsmann

For many years, the hall closet of my now-deceased parents' home was the storage area for numerous boxes of our family's photo albums. Only recently, had the boxes been passed around for nostalgic viewing by my siblings. Consequently, I had been busy perusing, scanning, editing and digitally saving pictures and enjoying the process immensely. I hadn't laid eyes on these pictures since I was a child.

Having been raised in a farm family with loving parents who showed their affection for each other as well as for us kids, we were a close-knit family. The pictures reflected this. My mom had a fair talent with the camera and my dad a fair tolerance for it. There were numerous pictures of joyful smiles, cuddled babies, birthday celebrations, First Communions and graduations. Then I came to the album leading up to 1966. I was six when my brother Michael became sick and had to endure cobalt treatments to battle his cancer. I was seven when he lost the fight. He was seventeen.

I found myself scanning and saving every single picture that had Mike in it, to try to remember him better, to never forget again. His face was familiar and yet, not so. I knew his eyes. They are my eyes, and my son's. As I flipped through the chronological pages of the album, gently remembering all my siblings and the places they each held in my little girl heart, I realized that I had come to the place in time where the words "Hodgkin's Disease" first crossed my parents' lips. I began searching for a knowing look on Mom and Dad's faces, signs of coming grief. I saw how infrequent their smiles became as my brother grew thinner and more gaunt. There is one picture in particular, of him up high on his stallion's back, only a few months before he died. His pencil-like legs gripped Prince's sides, his face a stony mask of illness. Through the open vee of his shirt, vivid red marks crisscrossed his neck–the telltale sign of cobalt treatments, the most advanced and brutal cancer weapon available in the 60's.

Michael knew he was sick, but did not know he was dying. This was my parents' wish. He was still worried about making up missed schoolwork so he could graduate with his class. Mom and Dad prayed for the miracle that would not come.

Now, a mother of two teenaged sons, I cannot even grapple with the possibility of enduring what my own mother faced. She knew she was losing her son. The cobalt treatments burned out his insides until only bile was left. How did she and my father not fall down in helpless grief and anguish? How did my older brothers and sister, who were old enough to comprehend the loss, continue to breathe, to work, to eat, to play with me?

Seeing pictures of Michael after so many years unearthed many tender memories: of him carrying me, tickling me, chasing me. Unexpectedly, a wave of grief washed over me as sudden as a surge of the ocean. My chest heaved and sobs nearly escaped my mouth, which I quickly stifled with my hand. My family was in the next room and I didn't want to alarm them. *This is crazy*, I thought. *He died nearly 40 years ago.* But only now was I fully feeling the grief and loss that I was too young to understand then. I was grieving 40 years late: for the life he might have lived had he been allowed to grow old, and for how all of our lives might have been different, better.

I gained a fuller understanding of what it took for my family to move on from his death that day in October. It was apparent in the photo album as well. There were no pictures from that next Christmas, and only a few graduation and birthday pictures for the next few years, always with one face missing. It broke my heart to see Dad's somber face and Mom's halfhearted smile–not like earlier pictures where their faces shone with joy.

I had no idea the emotional journey on which these old photos would take me. But I think it was a necessary one. Now I find Michael in my thoughts most every day. I ask him to help watch over my children and keep them safe, to be their guardian angel as he was my protective big brother. Now, years later, I am finally honoring him as he so deserves.

Mom and Dad kept many of the details of Michael's illness and death to themselves. One thing they did share with us was Michael's last words, which to this day continue to comfort and console me. When the Last Rites had been given and they were only waiting for the end, Michael quietly breathed, "Oh Mom, I'm *soooo* beautiful." And then he died.

– Geriann Fitzgerald

BLUEGRASS FESTIVAL

Drunken hillbilly
staggers among the
tents, always smiling.

Dancing with strangers,
he tips his hat to
the band and hollers.

Cooler full of beer-
part of his circuit.
Speaking too loudly,

he tells an older
couple about his
brother's recent death.

– Melany Nitzsche

HIDING IN THE SILENCE

"Mommy, what's a hijacker?"
Shocked as if I felt something crack
A sudden wave of sadness
Forces tears to fall
As I realize that your
Innocence had broken

I want to pretend I didn't hear
If I would stay silent
There would be nothing to fear
If I didn't answer
There would be no terror
Can I hide you from the truth?

We should talk about
The new kittens, make cookies
Or plan to rent a movie
Keep the rating of your life
Securely at 'PG'
But it's not so easy

Not wanting to expose you
To the sorrow and pain
I hesitate, but know I should
Try to explain...Remember
When you saw the planes crash?
No, it was no accident

Remember when we were
Snuggling close watching TV
And you felt my body jerk?
You asked, "What's wrong, Mommy?"
I could not come up with words to tell you
What I saw, but it was spelled W-A-R!

Now as we watch the picture of our lives
Change–from carefree to cautious
Even though I see that precious smile leave
As you wonder…Will things ever
Be the same? I know
I cannot hide you in the silence

9/11/2001

– Donna Schenk

No Voice

Standing before the auditorium
Students listened to her story
The stub awkwardly protruding
Where her right arm had been
Made the devastating description
Of the drunk driving collision
Brutally vivid
It got their attention
How much was taken from her

Candidly she told them in detail
How the horrific impact tore
The skin from her face and body
The once attractive teen shared
At times she feels like a freak
When she sees people stare
So much was taken, but
She was left with a powerful
Voice of experience

My best friend was in an accident
Like that, but there are no signs
Of pain after all this time
No one was there to see
How her head was smashed
She lost everything because
Of a drunk driver's crash
But she has no voice to say
How much was taken away

She'll never know special moments
Many often take for granted...
Squeezing my hand, as I trust her
With a secret that only she can keep
Feeling the warm breath on her neck
As her husband whispers his love
Or feeling a newborn's tight grip
On her finger, pulling on her heart
Every moment of intimacy was severed

Still haunted after years have passed
That others will never know the cost
Of a driver's choice to drink, because
There is no voice from the grave

– Donna Schenk

In Loving Memory of Lenore

THE SECRET WATERS AND THE MOON

The pain is now drifting through the fog of her mind, ever so lightly. No longer is it unbearable like that dark hole twisting her insides. The bottles are empty, like mismatched twins. They are her friends...helping her to forget.

It is okay like this, almost peaceful, like the quiet sounds of the night; its darkness hugging her in a sultry caress. She starts the "path of no return" feeling only relief, the patient moon her only companion.

She knows he could not possibly mean to hurt her like this! There was so much love and now it was gone. Like some strange force had overtaken his brain. She could tell by the emptiness in his once loving eyes.

Tears are running down her cheeks. Surrounded by stillness, she enters the water. The moon reflecting on the water is stirring an odd sense of familiarity in the far corners of her mind.

The moon is like God, always there; or is He? She is no longer mad at Him; He has the whole world to take care of. It's okay now...everything is okay now.

The water is warm and inviting, embracing her body like he used to. She closes her eyes and feels the serenity of her surroundings enter her bruised mind. Breathing very slowly, relaxing every muscle, her tension slowly drifts from her into the dark water. It is okay, it really is, and it is beautiful and painless.

When she looks up at the silent moon, she feels truly at peace. She is now floating on the tide of the moon. She becomes part of the moon. Her moves are soundless, effortless. The water pulls her under and she is tenderly swept away.

– Gea Pierce

TOMORROW

I walk away from security
Turn for a last look
At my nursing home room
My haven

Tomorrow no one will wake me
At six for a sponge bath
No one will check my vitals
Bring me my pills

No one will be waiting
Head bowed, half asleep
In the silent dining room
Rousing to greet me

No kind loving aide
Will lift me into bed
Draw up my blankets, say good night
Turn off my light

– *Elizabeth Hoffman*

The Myth of Me

after the last crisis resolves itself
Finally and Irrefutably

thank you notes written
flowers faded
bills paid

comes the quiet in a deafening roar

the only sound
accolades spilling over me
by family and friends and those familiar with
the circumstances we came to know as life

…he wouldn't have made it without you

no more pills to dispense
no side effects to make note of
no searching for the rising and falling of your belly
when you look so alarmingly peaceful as you rest

now there's just stillness…

the stillness we yearned for these past few years
when it remained so elusive

lately it pours over me in abundance

just like those saintly accolades
now told in past tense
the myth of me securely in place
and nothing to look forward to
but the inevitable descent

– Melany Nitzsche

EVERYWHERE I GO

Everywhere I go
I see bits of people lost to me
The back of a man's neck
The familiar hunch of
Humble shoulders, elbows
Leaning on a church pew
My father's unshaking faith

I feel envy when I see a mother
Touch her daughter's hair
Lovingly
As my mother did mine
So long ago

When I look at my son's
Tall, lanky frame, suntanned face
Deep brown eyes
I remember my brother lost to me
When he was but seventeen
And I a girl of seven

The silver spun hair
Of an old woman shyly smiling
Reminds me of my grandmother
And her gift of time to bake cookies
With this small, shy girl

The spirits of my loved ones
Are all around me
I need only to keep watching
And to always remember

– Geriann Fitzgerald

3rd Place Southwestern Illinois College
2005 Poetry Contest

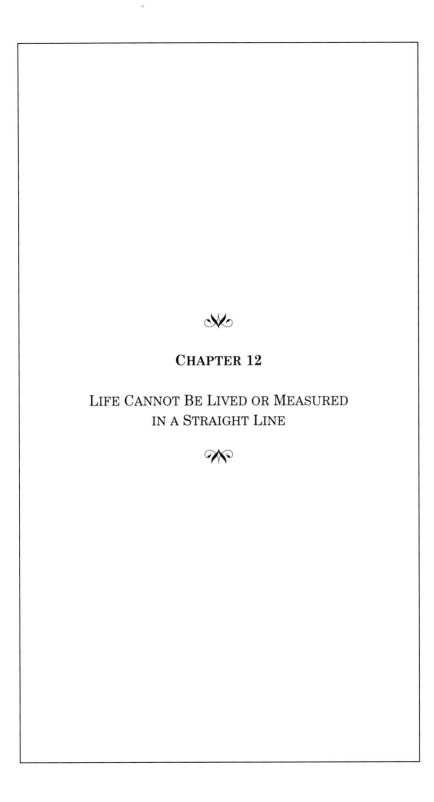

CHAPTER 12

LIFE CANNOT BE LIVED OR MEASURED IN A STRAIGHT LINE

SYNCHRONICITY

In the course of time
One comes to understand
That life, like love, cannot
be measured
In terms of linear experiences

Life consists, rather, of circular patterns
Ending and beginning, swirling and ebbing;
Every present event connected to the past
as well as to the future;
Every interaction filled with meaning and possibilities

An impulsive stop at the corner convenience store
Precipitates a chance meeting with an
Almost forgotten past acquaintance
And a life-altering occurrence results

A sudden memory from a childhood experience
Prolonged eye contact with a passing stranger
A vivid dream that awakens the sleeper with a start
The words and tune of a song that linger in the mind

Is a déjà vu experience merely an illusion?
Is a serendipitous discovery really made by accident?
And why does that new woman in the corner cubicle
seem so familiar?

It would be wise to instruct the little ones
To leave their twelve inch rulers
In their kindergarten desks
Life cannot be lived or measured
In a straight line

– Roselyn Mathews

MOLDING MINDS

Feeling feisty I face the day
    Ready again to connect images
    And fashion concepts
Striving to mold minds
    Not as metal that will not flex,
    But as pliable clay
Sensing the teachable moment
    I shelve my lesson plans
    To reach a greater height
Shifting paradigms takes time
    I am a piece of the puzzle
    Small part, but important
Feeling feisty I face the day
    Ready again to connect images
    And fashion concepts.

– Patricia Robert

IN A DIMMER PART

Regarding abuse in the foster care system

Crawl back under that rock.
You can't crush me with it anymore.
Dark nights don't hide darker eyes
and people are on to your sin.

The bones of me might break
but my fragile mind is on the mend.
I don't want your protection anymore.
It's done more harm than good.

I'll fly away from here, if only in my mind,
leaving thoughts of this shattered adolescence
in a dimmer part of my memory.
Only recalled to keep myself
a better man than you.

– Melany Nitzsche

THE LIGHT OF GRATITUDE

Awaking to misted sky
white fog softens my focus
soft snowy kisses
hover upon the land

Unannounced tears plummet
tumbling to the quiet place
tucked into a black corner
I have lost my way

Staring upon brisk solitude
on a frosted slice of horizon
I see each hour as a treasure
each moment as a miracle

Binding terms of humanity
permit a blink of existence
I am pertinent to those
who I touch in my time

It is a sin to breathe of life
yet wallow in worries and wants
when blessed with bounty
where gratitude should rule

Descending into the dusk
values grow apparent
dark accentuates light
I find my way free

– Lori Becherer

EASE AND CHARM

My life, like many, has been divided into definite segments, each with new joys, sorrows, challenges, and even different signatures. In 1947, as a divorced mother striving to succeed I was signing my name Elizabeth Bailey Burton, Home Advisor, Marion County. Home Advisors were the 40's counterparts of today's Martha Stewart. They worked with women and girls in the country and rural towns.

I remember one day vividly. It was a drizzly, dark Monday in mid-November. I had two missions: in the morning a sewing machine clinic, and in the afternoon a unit meeting at a neighboring farm house. There I would meet with the good ladies of the neighborhood and present a "lesson" on a topic the county program committees had chosen–*How to Achieve Ease and Charm as an Adult.*

The sewing machine clinic involved working with kerosene and oil. It was messy, so I chose to wear my airforce blue suit, almost ready for the cleaner. I had a fresh permanent. I thought my hair looked pretty good, and I could look presentable for my afternoon debut with the unit ladies. I had only been in the county since September.

After I had driven a mile I could see the meeting place surrounded by cars, a half mile to my right. I turned down the road, and had only gone ten feet when I realized I was stuck! Rocking back and forth only dug me in deeper. I jumped out of the car and opened the trunk, looking for something to put under my wheels to give me traction. The wind whipped out lesson sheets that I retrieved as I skidded around in the mud. Gathering up the sheets and my purse, I decided the show must go on...I would walk. My shoes were soon heavy with mud, so I thought the fence row would be better, only to find it filled with blackberry bushes that tore at my hose, leaving a long runner and a blurb of blood.

The ladies at the meeting must have been watching my wild approach. My hostess met me at the door, saying "Oh my goodness, you should have come from the other direction. The road is black topped that way. Never mind, my husband will tow you out with his tractor after the meeting. Take your shoes off. I'll get you my husband's house slippers."

She led me into the living room, where my new clients, eager to make a good impression, were in their Sunday best black crepes with pearls, and the faint aroma of Cashmere Bouquet and Evening in Paris perfumed the room.

I was introduced and stood there, smelling to high heaven of kerosene and permanent fluid, a large spot of oil on my bosom, frizzy hair, makeup long blown and washed from my face, hose full of runners over bloody legs spattered with mud. The piece de resistance was the duck-like men's slippers that adorned my feet!

It took guts to begin my lesson with this statement: "To have ease and charm, at all times you must be well groomed."

No one laughed, and at that moment I was aware of how understanding and kind rural women are. I also learned two valuable lessons that day. Life has its own way of slapping you down when you get too self-important. Most important, to survive you must be able to laugh at yourself...I still laugh.

– Elizabeth Hoffman

From the Third Floor Balcony

Corseted in the steam of August
She stood on a third floor balcony
With eyes squinted

Far out at sea,
Near the place where ships fall off
Gray, foreboding clouds
Hinted at a storm brewing

Closer in, silhouetted against the horizon
A fleet of white fishing boats drifted eastward
Noisy sea gulls floating, swooping
Circled the boats
Lusting for an easy breakfast

At the shore line
Blue and turquoise waves
Tipped with crystal foam
Quietly exploded
According to the sea's rhythm

On the uncluttered beach
A mother watched her baby
Crawl like a crab in the sugar-white sand
His hands exploring the change in texture
As he approached the churning, crashing surf

On the third floor balcony
Above swelling dunes and swaying sea oats
The God-like woman saw all these things

Yet, controlled nothing

– Roselyn Mathews

Notable Entry Saturday Writers Chapter
Missouri Writers Guild
2003 One-Page Poetry Contest

MOSAIC

Shattering mirror
    window of the soul
        shattering, tattering, battering
World of regrets
    unstable, unsure, unclear
        each fragment precious, yet broken

Ways to self-correct?
Ways to repair damage done?
Ways to grasp reality from a deeper pool?

What epoxy can reconstruct?
Is there peace in reconstruction
when no immutable restoration occurs?

What's this broken mirror worth?
The shreds remain shiny
The shards can prevail

Become a mosaic...

Shattered yet beautiful
Fragments in disarray

Fill in missing pieces
with glorious colored tiles

Epoxy the pieces
    with precise care

Not whole again, yet valuable,
    cherished and loved

– Patricia Robert

BOXED IN

We are folded
   Molded
      Upholstered
         Rolled in
A form-fitting box.

The translucent dreams are
   Waiting
      Creating
         Ambulating
Just atop the box.

Squiggle your arm on up
Spiral your hand on through
Rise with phoenix-flight
Bathed in golden light.

– Patricia Robert

PORTRAIT IN SEPIA

Forlorn face, abandoned wife
A survivor with wounds exposed
Wiry eyebrows crawling in all directions
Graceless, evident age, with an almost cauliflower nose

Smooth hat contradicting hard, thickened skin
Traveled many miles, unashamed of where he's been

Decisions made with drunken defiance
A life made harder by choice
Surprised to grow old in spite of himself
Wasted refuge, haggard life

– Melany Nitzsche

3rd Place Southwestern Illinois College
2003 Poetry Contest

WOMEN, TODAY AND TOMORROW

Who is today's woman? Is it my granddaughter, a neophyte in the business of living, full of dreams, living with a natural simplicity that defies convention, sure that somehow, somewhere, she will be provided for? Is it my daughter, whose days are filled with the responsibility for a large family, a legally blind husband and a job? She finds time to be special to each of her children. Her joy in life attracts young and old to her. Is it, in a small way, still me? After all, I'm a contemporary of our president and first lady, so I'm still part of the scene.*

I'm ahead of my generation in many ways. I have a college degree. I was a married and pregnant student (in that order) in a day when this was almost unheard of. A divorce at thirty forced me to become an independent professional woman. I reared my two children alone. A beautiful second marriage ended with my widowhood, so again I am independent. I am retired after thirty years spent in a satisfying career.

I can remember when few fields were open to women. You could teach, or nurse, or be a domestic, or perhaps clerk in a store. The more daring might venture into the business world as a secretary, or even open a millinery store. A woman teacher who married was immediately dismissed, and an unmarried teacher who became pregnant was a disgrace too terrible to be mentioned.

By the time I started working, things had changed. More fields were open, but wages certainly were not equal. Today the situation is continually improving. A woman can qualify for almost any job...and is doing so. Salaries for men and women are more nearly equal. A woman's career is limited only by her ability, ambition and willingness to give her all to her work. Success may not come quickly, and competition may be rough. Brought up in a permissive, opulent society, accustomed to instant gratification, today's young woman will need to change attitudes and expectations if she is to reach her career goal. This is good.

Life could be difficult for her in even more important ways. Never before has a woman been faced with so many vital decisions. Social mores made decisions for yesterday's young woman. When I was young, a female was automatically considered a "lady," no matter her age – precious and revered for that reason. Hats were tipped, doors opened, heavy parcels carried, her honor protected, laws passed to protect her working conditions. No "nice" girls went into bars; no "nice" girls had sex before marriage. Education and a career were stepping stones to her real goal–successful marriage and motherhood. The relevance of

157

religion and patriotism were undisputed. It was a secure and comfortable world.

Today that security is gone. Today's woman opens her own doors, carries her own bundles, goes into bars, has sex if she chooses. She gives top priority to the goal of a successful career in many cases. Marriage and motherhood have their place in her life, but must be accommodated to her work needs. She questions the advisability of bringing children into an overpopulated world, and knows that she will not be forced by circumstance into childbearing. Her observation of broken and unhappy marriages in her parents' generation leads her to consider other forms of "meaningful" relationships. She questions the materialistic values of her parents, but accepts material support from that generation. She is disillusioned by the rottenness she sees in political life, so she questions the validity of patriotism. She questions the religious beliefs of her parents.

This is the young woman who begins her adult life as our nation begins its third century. She is the granddaughter of my generation, so in many ways I feel responsible for her. She is healthy; she is bright; she is beautiful; she is aware. Her great great great granddaughter will be her age when our third century closes. So much depends on her and the generations of women who will follow her lead. I am frightened for her. I pray she will make the right choices.

Will she choose to become a neuter person, denying the God given qualities that make her special–her capacity for giving, for loving, for understanding, for compassion, for nurturing and teaching the young? Will she give last priority to creating a home for those she loves? Will she flit from one "meaningful" relationship to another? Will she decide a child might frustrate her, interfere with her career, deny her of material possessions? She will demand her rights, collect top pay, perform superbly in her work...but in doing so, will she put self realization at the top of her priority list? As she chooses to compete with her male contemporaries, will she excel them, crowd them out and humiliate them? Will she feel too self sufficient to need a religious faith, too sophisticated to be patriotic?

If this is the path she follows, her life will end in loneliness, frustration, disillusionment and regret.

I hope she chooses the other path open to her...that of never denying her femininity. I wish for her a satisfying career, one that is well paid, but one that does not consume her or destroy others. I wish for her the satisfaction of accomplishing good things, for her family, on her job, in her community, her church, her nation, her world, without once caring who gets the credit so long as the job is done. I wish for her marriage and the love of a good man, but most of all that she may love unselfishly. I wish for her children to nurture (perhaps not born to her but hers through love). I wish for her a home of her making...a haven for those she loves. I wish for her sound values that put people before things, others before self. I wish for her a family bound together by love and mutual respect, not by necessity. I wish for her a beautiful and deep religious faith.

If this is the path she follows, she will be able to look back on her life with joy and satisfaction; her family will be a blessing to her and loneliness will never be her lot. It will be women of her kind who will help to lead our country safely and successfully through its third century. I wish these things for her because I love her, because I love my country. I pray that the life she chooses to live will be a blessing to the generations of women who may find inspiration in her example.

– Elizabeth Hoffman

*written in 1973

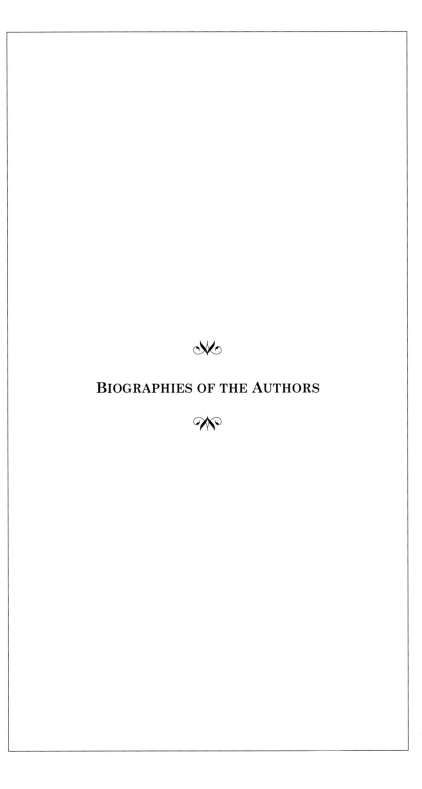

BIOGRAPHIES OF THE AUTHORS

LORI BECHERER has been actively writing since 1989 when she started her first daily journal. She is a relentless gardener who loves the tiny discoveries that live within her gardens. Most of her poetry and essays evolve from daily observations and journal entries. She resides on her childhood farm near Millstadt, Illinois with her husband of 23 years. In addition to writing and gardening, Lori also enjoys painting, portraiture and dream journaling. She has been published in *Personal Journaling* magazine and several times in health information journals and periodicals. Lori is employed full time as Assistant Director of the Health Information Department at Belleville Memorial Hospital.

MEG BERGMANN is a native of south St. Louis County. Having formerly tackled such varied tasks as California beach bumming, wild animal rescue and rehabilitation, and television news, she now devotes her time to writing, veterinary assisting, and family. Meg currently resides along with her husband and their two children in Columbia, Illinois.

LUCY ENGBRING was born in Milwaukee, Wisconsin, but Valmeyer, Illinois has been her home for the last 38 years. She boasts 57 years of marriage "to the same man, of course!" She joined the Marine Corps during World War II, and spent most of her married life as a military wife. After earning degrees from the University of Wisconsin and McKendree College, she taught reading in the Valmeyer school district. She wrote features for the *Waterloo Republic-Time*s for many years, and continues freelance writing. She and her husband Jerry have eleven children. With the nest now empty, she has more time to read, write, travel, play piano at the Care Center, and just enjoy being "a recycled teenager."

GERIANN "GERI" FITZGERALD grew up on a grain and dairy farm in St. Rose, Illinois. She now resides in Waterloo, Illinois with her husband and their two teenaged sons. Geri has worked full time for a nearby utility company for twenty-six years, and in her spare time she enjoys writing, reading, walking trails, and most of all, spending time with her family.

ELIZABETH "BETTY" HOFFMAN is a retired Home Economist. She began painting and writing as retirement projects and attended painting workshops in exotic locales such as Bermuda, Greece, Ireland, Switzerland, England and Arizona. Her watercolor paintings have been displayed at numerous local shows. Betty was born in 1913 and has two children, nine grandchildren and eighteen great-grandchildren.

Teacher, poet and dreamer, ROSELYN MATHEWS grew up on a picturesque farm in southern Illinois. The innate beauty of the rural setting of her childhood still strongly influences her writing. A former high school English teacher, Roselyn considers herself a perpetual student of life. She teaches creative writing and personal development classes at St. Louis Community College at Meramec and at Southwestern Illinois College. Roselyn founded the Heartland Women's Writers Guild in 1998.

MELANY NITZSCHE worked as a CPA for almost 10 years before escaping to save her sanity. She currently serves on the Board of Directors of the Missouri Lupus Foundation and has been active in fundraising for brain tumor research. She also enjoys traveling, reading, writing, earth-friendly living, and obsessive organizing. She credits her dad for her sense of curiosity, making her an expert at nothing, yet interested in everything. In that same vein, she is currently a student of literature at Webster University.

ELIZABETH "LIZ" PARKER lived in Australia, Arizona, North Carolina and Chicago before returning to the Alton, Illinois area where she was born and raised. After teaching and practicing in hospital critical care units for over 15 years, she earned a Juris Doctorate degree from Arizona State University. She currently practices law in Illinois and Missouri. She has two daughters, Brigit and Meredith. In addition to writing, she studies Flamenco dance, practices yoga, and with her fiancé Jerry, enjoys horses and motorcycle riding. Her lively family, varied homes, careers, and extensive travels provide rich material for her writing.

GEA PIERCE is the oldest of six children and was born, raised and educated in The Netherlands, Europe. She moved to the USA in 1973 after marrying an American in 1971. She was employed as a teacher in The Netherlands, Arizona and in Missouri, before opening a photography studio in Waterloo with her husband. They divorced in 1985. She remarried in 1990 and became a mother at 42. Reading and writing have always been important in her life.

PATRICIA "PAT" ROBERT has taught reading and English courses at Red Bud, Illinois, and before that, at Dieterich, Illinois. She has longed to write a book since she was a young girl. Her publishing credits include articles and poems in publications for teachers and inspirational magazines. During the 1980's, she was a correspondent to the *Effingham Daily News*. Joining the Heartland Women's Writers Guild has been a catalyst that has helped her grow as a writer.

A volunteer for Hospice, DONNA SCHENK wrote her first poem to express feelings at the loss of her first patient. That poem won 2nd place in a Southwestern Illinois College poetry contest. Over time, writing poetry has become a passion for Donna. Her poems have placed in a variety of contests, including "Poet of the Month" by QB Publishing and 1st Place in the St. Louis Writer's Guild Poetry Contest. Donna gives credit to God for inspiration, the Heartland Women's Writers Guild for encouragement, and her six children for loving support.

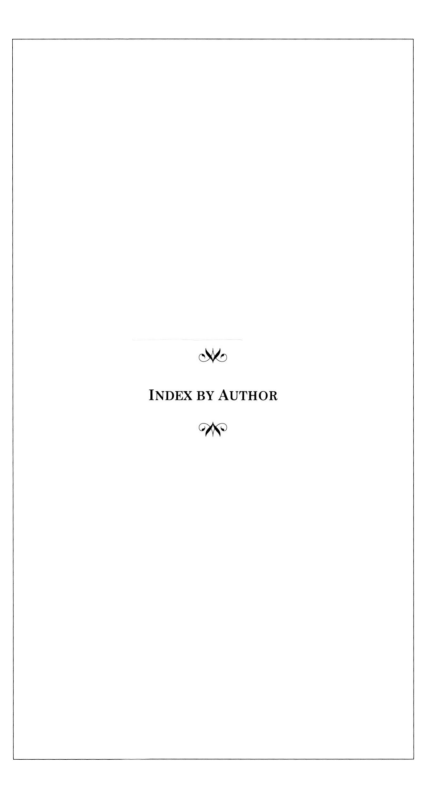

INDEX BY AUTHOR

LORI BECHERER

MEG BERGMANN

LUCY ENGBRING

ROSELYN MATHEWS

MELANY NITZSCHE

ELIZABETH PARKER

GEA PIERCE

PATRICIA ROBERT

DONNA SCHENK

INDEX

A

B

C

D

W

Y